C000144788

INTRODUCTION ...

A few points about this revision guide ...

● It is matched perfectly to the new specification from AQA:

SCIENCE: DOUBLE AWARD COORDINATED - Specification B

So it contains everything the pupil needs to know, ...

        ... and nothing more.

● The 'Contents' pages are cross-referenced to the specification reference.

● Each section is condensed into a single 'Key Points' page. This enables a quick final recap prior to examination and also builds pupils' confidence in that they can see their task before them on a single page.

● Each section concludes with a set of summary questions. These are, of necessity, brief but can be supplemented by our brilliant volume of 'pupil worksheets' which are written page for page to this guide (see inside back cover).

● Slang words and colloquialisms are avoided in favour of plain, good old-fashioned English.

● The new layout, with improved diagrams, provides a more spacious, user-friendly feel.

● 'The Earth and Beyond' and 'Forces and Motion' are combined to form one 'Key Points' page and 'Summary Questions' section.

● The reduction in the amount of 'Higher' material in the new specification means that it makes more sense than ever before to combine both 'Higher' and 'Foundation' material in the one guide. This, of course, allows much greater flexibility in switching between tiers.

> ═══════════════════════════════════ HIGHER TIER ═
> **All the 'Higher' material is clearly indicated by RED boxes.**

Mary James

Mary James – **Editor**

• CONTENTS

CONTENTS

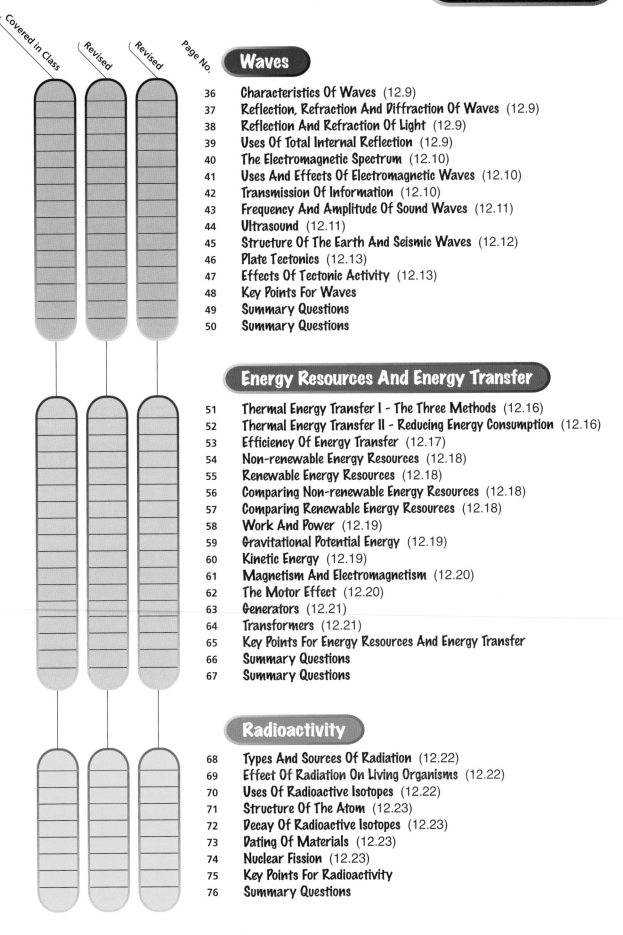
*Numbers in brackets refer to Specification reference numbers

HOW TO USE THIS REVISION GUIDE

- Don't just sit back and read this guide. Learn actively by constantly testing yourself without looking at the text.

- When you have revised a small sub-section or a diagram, PLACE A BOLD TICK AGAINST IT, and also tick the 'Covered In Class' and 'Revised' sections of the contents pages as you progress.
This is great for your self-confidence.

- Jot down anything which will help you to remember – no matter how trivial it may seem.

- Use the actual pages within a section for your revision and link them to the information in the 'Key Points' pages. Only use the 'Key Points' pages on their own for a last minute recap before your examination.

HIGHER TIER

ONLY PUPILS DOING HIGHER TIER SHOULD REVISE THE MATERIAL IN THE RED BOXES.

SOME IMPORTANT FACTS ABOUT YOUR EXAMINATION

- You will have THREE PAPERS lasting 1 HOUR 30 MINUTES EACH.

- Each paper will consist of 90 marks and represent $26^2/3$ % of the total marks available.

- All papers will consist of compulsory structured questions of different lengths, incorporating calculations and data-response, and will provide opportunities for answers written in continuous prose.
The marking of these will take into account the quality of written communication.

- Candidates may use a calculator for all three papers.

    PAPER 1: LIFE PROCESSES AND LIVING THINGS
    PAPER 2: MATERIALS AND THEIR PROPERTIES
    PAPER 3: PHYSICAL PROCESSES

FORMULA					PAGE No.
Potential Difference (volt, V)	=	Current (ampere, A)	x	Resistance (ohm, Ω)	$V = IR$	8
Power (watt, W)	=	Potential Difference (volt, V)	x	Current (ampere, A)	$P = VI$	9, 64
Energy Transferred (kilowatt hour, kWh)	=	Power (kilowatt, W)	x	Time (Hour, h)	$E = Pt$	14
Total Cost	=	Number of Units	x	Cost per Unit		14
Energy Transferred (joule, J)	=	Power (watt, W)	x	Time (second, s)	$E = Pt$	13
Speed (metre/second, m/s)	=	$\dfrac{\text{Distance Travelled (metre, m)}}{\text{Time Taken (second, s)}}$			$s = \dfrac{d}{t}$	21
Acceleration (metre/second squared, m/s²)	=	$\dfrac{\text{Change in Velocity (metre/second m/s)}}{\text{Time Taken For Change (second, s)}}$			$a = \dfrac{v - u}{t}$	22
Wave Speed (metre/second, m/s)	=	Frequency (hertz, Hz)	x	Wavelength (metre, m)	$v = f\lambda$	36
Efficiency	=	$\dfrac{\text{Useful Energy Transferred By Device}}{\text{Total Energy Supplied To Device}}$				53
Work Done	=	Energy Transferred				58
Work Done (joule, J)	=	Force Applied (Newton, N)	x	Distance Moved In Direction Of Force (metre, m)	$W = Fs$	58
Power (watt, W)	=	$\dfrac{\text{Work Done (joule, J)}}{\text{Time Taken (second, s)}}$			$P = \dfrac{W}{t}$	58
Weight (newton, N)	=	Mass (kilogram, kg)	x	Gravitational Field Strength (newton/kilogram, N/kg)	$w = mg$	59

HIGHER TIER

Change in Gravitational Potential Energy (joule, J)	=	Weight (newton, N)	x	Change in Vertical Height (metre, m)	$gpe = mg\Delta h$	59
Kinetic Energy (joule, J)	= ½ x	Mass (kilogram, kg)	x	Speed² [(metre/second)², (m/s)²]	$ke = \frac{1}{2}mv^2$	60
Energy Transferred (joule, J)	=	Potential Difference (volt, V)	x	Charge (coulomb, C)	$E = VQ$	9
Charge (coulomb, C)	=	Current (ampere, A)	x	Time (second, s)	$Q = It$	9
Force (newton, N)	=	Mass (kilogram, kg)	x	Acceleration (metre/second squared, m/s²)	$F = ma$	25
$\dfrac{\text{Voltage Across Primary (volt, V)}}{\text{Voltage Across Secondary (volt, V)}}$	=	$\dfrac{\text{Number Of Turns On Primary}}{\text{Number Of Turns On Secondary}}$			$\dfrac{V_p}{V_s} = \dfrac{N_p}{N_s}$	64

An **ELECTRIC CURRENT** will flow through an **ELECTRICAL COMPONENT** (or device) ...
... if there is a **VOLTAGE** or **POTENTIAL DIFFERENCE** (p.d.) across the ends of the component.
In the following circuits each cell and lamp are identical ...

CIRCUIT 1

Cell provides p.d. ...
... across the lamp.

A current flows and ...
... the lamp lights up.

The amount of current that flows through the component above depends on two things ...

1. The Potential Difference (p.d.) Across The Component

The **GREATER** the **POTENTIAL DIFFERENCE** or **VOLTAGE** across a component ...
... the **GREATER** the **CURRENT** that flows through the component.

CIRCUIT 2

Two cells together provide ...
... a bigger p.d. across the lamp.

A bigger current now flows and ...
... the lamp lights up more brightly...
... compared to circuit 1.

2. The Resistance Of The Component

COMPONENTS RESIST the **FLOW** of **CURRENT THROUGH THEM.** They have **RESISTANCE.**
The **GREATER** the **RESISTANCE** of a **COMPONENT** or **COMPONENTS** ...

... the **SMALLER** the **CURRENT** that ...
... flows for a **PARTICULAR VOLTAGE.**

OR

... the **GREATER** the **VOLTAGE** needed ...
... to maintain a **PARTICULAR CURRENT.**

CIRCUIT 3

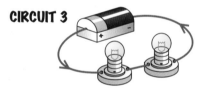

Two lamps together have a **GREATER RESISTANCE.**
A smaller current now flows and ...
... the lamps light up less brightly (compared to circuit 1).

CIRCUIT 4

Two cells together provide a **GREATER VOLTAGE** ...
... and the same current as in circuit 1 will now flow and ...
... the lamps light up more brightly (compared to circuit 3).

Measurement Of Potential Difference And Current

The potential difference (p.d.)
across a component in a circuit
is measured in volts (V)
using a **VOLTMETER** connected
in **PARALLEL** across
the component.

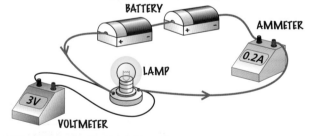

BATTERY
AMMETER
0.2A
LAMP
3V
VOLTMETER

The current flowing through
a component in a circuit
is measured in amperes (A),
using an **AMMETER**
connected in **SERIES.**

Standard Symbols For Drawing Circuit Diagrams

The following standard symbols should be known. You may be asked to interpret and/or draw circuits
using the following standard symbols.

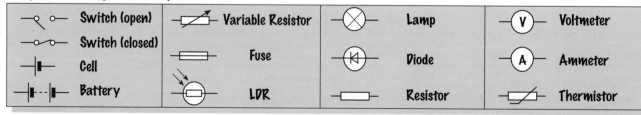

Switch (open)	Variable Resistor	Lamp	Voltmeter
Switch (closed)			
Cell	Fuse	Diode	Ammeter
Battery	LDR	Resistor	Thermistor

Components Connected In Series

In a series circuit, ALL COMPONENTS are connected ONE AFTER THE OTHER in ONE LOOP, going from ONE TERMINAL of the BATTERY to the OTHER. When components are connected in series ...

1 The same CURRENT flows through each COMPONENT.

ie. $A_1 = A_2 = A_3$

eg. each ammeter reading is 0.1A.

2 The POTENTIAL DIFFERENCE (p.d.) or VOLTAGE ...
... supplied by the battery is DIVIDED UP ...
... between the TWO COMPONENTS in the circuit.

ie. $V_1 = V_2 + V_3$

However ...
... in our circuit both bulbs have the same resistance and the voltage is ...
... divided equally, but if one bulb had twice the resistance of the other, ...
... then the voltage would be divided differently ie. 2V and 1V.

3 Each component has a RESISTANCE and ...
... the TOTAL RESISTANCE is the sum of ...
... each individual resistance added together.
eg. if both P and Q each have a resistance of 15 ohms ...
... the total resistance = 15 ohms + 15 ohms = 30 ohms.

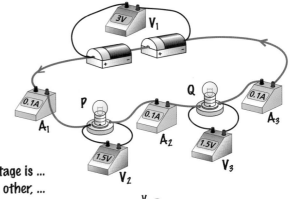

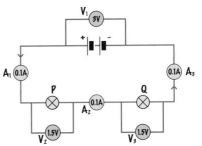

Components Connected In Parallel

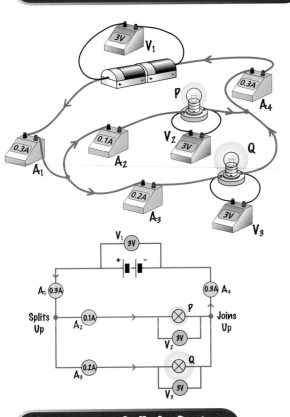

Components connected in parallel are connected SEPARATELY in their OWN LOOP going from ONE TERMINAL of the BATTERY to the OTHER. When components are connected in parallel ...

(1) The TOTAL CURRENT in the main circuit ...
... is equal to the SUM of the CURRENTS ...
... through the separate components.

ie. $A_1 = A_2 + A_3 = A_4$

eg. 0.3A = 0.1A + 0.2A = 0.3A

(2) The POTENTIAL DIFFERENCE ACROSS ...
... EACH COMPONENT is the SAME.
(... and is equal to the p.d. of the battery)

ie. $V_1 = V_2 = V_3$

eg. each bulb has a p.d. of 3V across it.

(3) The AMOUNT OF CURRENT which passes ...
... through EACH COMPONENT depends on the ...
... RESISTANCE OF EACH COMPONENT.
The greater the resistance, the smaller the current.
Bulb P has TWICE the RESISTANCE of bulb Q ...
... and so only 0.1A passes through bulb P ...
... while 0.2A passes through bulb Q.

Connecting Cells In Series

The TOTAL POTENTIAL DIFFERENCE provided by cells CONNECTED in SERIES is the SUM of the P.D. ...
... of EACH CELL SEPARATELY, providing that they have been connected in the same direction.
Each of the following cells has a p.d. of 1.5V ...

Total p.d. = 2 x 1.5V = 3V   Total p.d. = 3 x 1.5V = 4.5V

V = IR

RESISTANCE is a measure of how hard it is to get a CURRENT
through a component at a PARTICULAR POTENTIAL DIFFERENCE or VOLTAGE.
Potential difference, current and resistance are related by the formula:

POTENTIAL DIFFERENCE (volt, V) = CURRENT (ampere, A) x RESISTANCE (ohm, Ω)

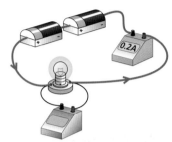

Example

Calculate the reading on the voltmeter in the circuit opposite
if the bulb has a resistance of 15 ohms.

Using our formula: POTENTIAL DIFFERENCE = CURRENT x RESISTANCE

= 0.2A x 15Ω

= 3V

(we use the letter I for current)

$$\frac{V}{I \times R}$$

> The reading on the ammeter is the current.

Resistance Of Components

These can be investigated using the circuit above with a power pack instead of batteries.
You could then draw CURRENT-VOLTAGE graphs which show how the CURRENT THROUGH
the component varies with the VOLTAGE ACROSS IT.

❶ RESISTOR

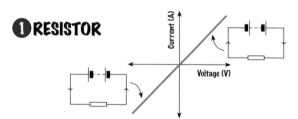

Providing the TEMPERATURE of the RESISTOR ...

... STAYS CONSTANT then ...

... THE CURRENT THROUGH THE RESISTOR IS PROPORTIONAL
TO THE VOLTAGE ACROSS THE RESISTOR ...

... ie. if one doubles, the other doubles etc ...

... regardless of which direction the current is flowing.

❷ FILAMENT LAMP

As the TEMPERATURE of the ...

... FILAMENT INCREASES and the ...

... bulb gets brighter then the ...

... RESISTANCE OF THE FILAMENT LAMP INCREASES, ...

... regardless of which direction the current is flowing.

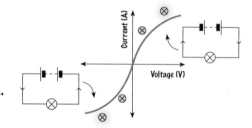

❸ DIODE

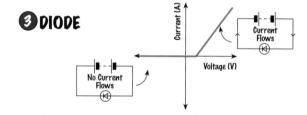

A diode allows a CURRENT to flow through it ...

... in ONE DIRECTION ONLY.

It has a VERY HIGH RESISTANCE ...

... in the REVERSE DIRECTION ...

... and no current flows.

Two Other Components

LIGHT DEPENDENT RESISTOR (LDR)

The resistance of an LDR ...

... depends on the amount of light falling on it.

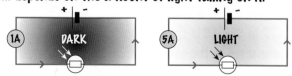

Its RESISTANCE DECREASES as the ...

... AMOUNT OF LIGHT FALLING ON IT INCREASES.

This allows more current to flow.

THERMISTOR

The resistance of a Thermistor ...

... depends on its temperature.

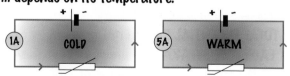

Its RESISTANCE DECREASES as the ...

... TEMPERATURE OF THE THERMISTOR INCREASES.

This allows more current to flow.

Power And Energy Transfer

An electric current is a flow of charge which transfers energy from the battery or power supply ...
... to the components in the circuit. If the component is a resistor, electrical energy is transferred as heat.
The RATE of this ENERGY TRANSFER is the POWER of the component or appliance ...
... and is measured in joules/second or WATTS (W) where 1 watt is the transfer of 1 joule
of energy in 1 second. Power is calculated using the following formula ...

POWER (W) = POTENTIAL DIFFERENCE (V) x CURRENT (A)

Most appliances have a rating plate on them which gives us their maximum power and their working voltage.
We can then calculate the current passing through the appliance and therefore the ideal current rating of the
fuse in the circuit.

POWER   P.D. (VOLTAGE)
↓   ↓

```
900W          230v-50Hz
WELLMAN
SUPERSTEAM
SERIAL No 6161623PW
```

DOMESTIC IRON RATING PLATE

Using our formula:
(rearranged
using formula triangle)

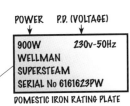

$$CURRENT = \frac{POWER}{POTENTIAL\ DIFFERENCE}$$

$$= \frac{900W}{230V}$$

$$= 3.9\ amps.$$

And, the CURRENT RATING of the fuse should be 5amps. Ideally it should be as close as possible
to (but HIGHER than) the normal current which flows through the appliance (see P.11)

▰▰▰ HIGHER TIER ▰▰▰

Charge And Energy Transfer

The amount of electrical CHARGE which passes ANY POINT in a circuit is measured in Coulombs (C) and depends on ...
... the CURRENT that flows and the TIME for which the current flows.

Charge, current and time are related by the formula:

CHARGE (C) = CURRENT (A) x TIME (s)

Here is a simple circuit ...

(Q represents charge)

If the circuit above is switched on for 40 seconds and a current of 0.5 Amps flows, then ...

... using the formula: CHARGE   =   CURRENT x TIME
                      =   0.5A x 40s
                      =   20 coulombs

> ... THIS AMOUNT OF CHARGE GOES PAST ANY POINT IN THE CIRCUIT IN THE 40 SECONDS.

However ...
As this CHARGE PASSES THROUGH THE BULB AN ENERGY TRANSFER TAKES PLACE.
The amount of ENERGY TRANSFERRED BY EVERY COULOMB of charge depends on the SIZE of the SUPPLY VOLTAGE!
THE GREATER the SUPPLY VOLTAGE the GREATER the ENERGY TRANSFERRED by EVERY COULOMB OF CHARGE.

Energy transferred, potential difference and charge are related by the formula:

ENERGY TRANSFERRED (J) = POTENTIAL DIFFERENCE (V) x CHARGE (C)

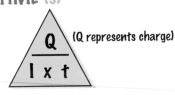

If we go back to our circuit above which was switched on for 40 seconds then ...

ENERGY TRANSFERRED   =   P.D. x CHARGE
                          =   1.5V x 20C
                          =   30 joules ...

> ... THIS AMOUNT OF ELECTRICAL ENERGY IS TRANSFERRED BY THE BULB TO LIGHT AND HEAT ENERGY.

REMEMBER   The charge has gained this energy from the supply voltage ie. the battery ...
                   ... which it then transfers to the bulb in the 40 secs the circuit was switched on!

Most electrical appliances are connected to the MAINS ELECTRICITY SUPPLY ...

... using a CABLE and a 3-PIN PLUG which is inserted into a SOCKET on the ring main circuit.

In the UK, the mains supply has a VOLTAGE OF ABOUT 230 VOLTS ...

... which if it's not used safely can kill!!

MAINS SUPPLY BY SOCKET

3-PIN PLUG

CABLE

A typical appliance - a kettle

3-Pin Plug

EARTH WIRE (Green & Yellow)
- All appliances with outer metal cases are earthed.

NEUTRAL WIRE (Blue)
- Carries current away from appliance.

CABLE GRIP
- Secures the cable in the plug.

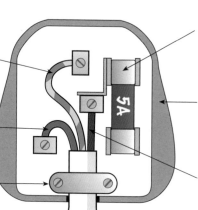

FUSE
- Always part of the live circuit.
- Should be of the proper current rating.

CASING
- Plastic or Rubber because both are good insulators.

LIVE WIRE (Brown)
- Carries current to appliance.

- Inner cores of COPPER ...
- ... because it's a good conductor.
- Outer layers of FLEXIBLE PLASTIC ...
- ... because it's a good insulator.

CABLE

WIRES   CABLE

PINS

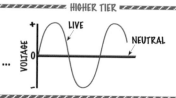

CASING

- The plug has ...
- ... PINS made from BRASS ...
- ... because it's a good conductor.

NB

━━━ HIGHER TIER ━━━

The LIVE terminal of the mains supply alternates between ...

... a positive and negative voltage with respect to the NEUTRAL terminal, ...

... which stays at a voltage close to zero with respect to EARTH.

VOLTAGE LIVE NEUTRAL 0 + –

Errors In Wiring Plugs

It is very important that all plugs are wired correctly with NO errors, for our own safety.

Below are five examples of dangerously wired plugs!

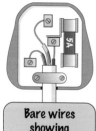

Bare wires showing

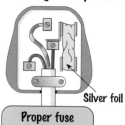

Silver foil

Proper fuse not installed

Earth wire not connected

Live and neutral wrong way round

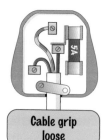

Cable grip loose

Dangerous Practices In The Use Of Mains Electricity

Apart from making sure that all plugs are wired correctly, here are some 'common sense' practices which should be followed at all times:
- All broken plugs and frayed cables should be replaced.
- Keep plugs and cables away from water or heat.
- Never overload a socket with too many plugs.
- Make sure your hands aren't wet when switching appliances on or off.

Alternating Current

This type of current changes direction of flow back and forth continuously. The number of complete cycles of reversal per second is called the **FREQUENCY**, and for mains electricity this is 50 cycles per second (Hertz). **FREQUENCY** and **VOLTAGE** can be compared using an oscilloscope.

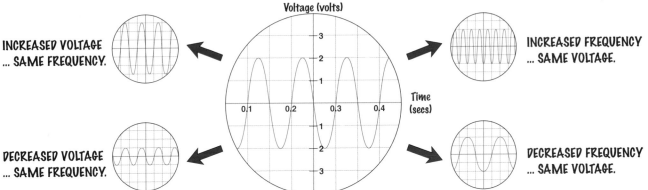

INCREASED VOLTAGE ... SAME FREQUENCY.

INCREASED FREQUENCY ... SAME VOLTAGE.

DECREASED VOLTAGE ... SAME FREQUENCY.

DECREASED FREQUENCY ... SAME VOLTAGE.

In the main example above, the peak voltage is 2 volts and the frequency is 10 cycles per second since one complete cycle takes 0.1 seconds.

Direct Current

This type of current always flows in the same direction. Cells and batteries supply d.c. We can use an oscilloscope to compare the voltage of different d.c. supplies.

INCREASING VOLTAGE

Fuses

A **FUSE** is a **SHORT, THIN** piece of **WIRE** with a **LOW MELTING POINT**.
When the **CURRENT** passing through it **EXCEEDS** the **CURRENT RATING** of the fuse, ...
... the fuse wire gets **HOT** and **MELTS** or **BREAKS**.
This **PREVENTS DAMAGE** to the **CABLE** or the **APPLIANCE** through the possibility of **OVERHEATING**.

3-AMP   13 AMP

CURRENT LARGER THAN CURRENT RATING OF FUSE → FUSE BURNS OUT → CIRCUIT IS BROKEN → NO CURRENT FLOWS → CABLE OR APPLIANCE IS PROTECTED

However ...   • For this safety system to work properly the **CURRENT RATING** of the fuse ...
     • ... must be **JUST ABOVE THE NORMAL WORKING CURRENT** of the appliance (see P.9)

Example Of A Fuse In Action

Normally the current flowing ...
... is <u>BELOW</u> the current rating ...
... of the fuse ...
... and the appliance (hairdrier) ...
... works properly.
However ...
... a fault occurs inside the appliance ...

... and the live wire makes contact ...
... with the neutral wire.
The current now flowing is <u>ABOVE</u>
... the current rating of the fuse ...
... because there is less resistance.
This causes the fuse wire to get ...
... hotter and hotter until ...

... it gets so hot ...
... it melts!
The circuit is now broken.
No current flows and ...
... there is no danger of ...
... further damage to the appliance ...
... or injury to the user.

Circuit Breakers

Most modern houses tend to have **CIRCUIT BREAKERS** rather than rely on fuses in the consumer unit.
- They depend on an **ELECTROMAGNET** which separates a **PAIR OF CONTACTS** ...
- ... **WHEN THE CURRENT BECOMES HIGH ENOUGH.**
- They work **MORE QUICKLY THAN A FUSE,** ...
- ... and are **EASILY RESET** by pressing a button.

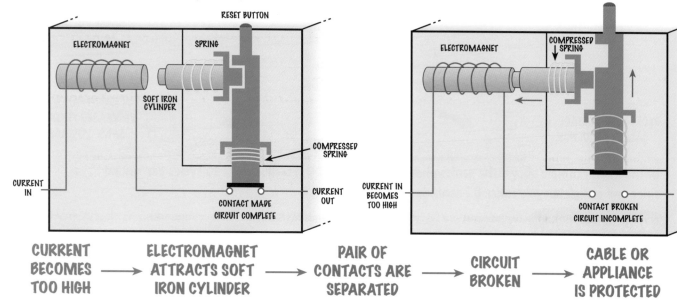

| CURRENT BECOMES TOO HIGH | → | ELECTROMAGNET ATTRACTS SOFT IRON CYLINDER | → | PAIR OF CONTACTS ARE SEPARATED | → | CIRCUIT BROKEN | → | CABLE OR APPLIANCE IS PROTECTED |

Many houses though still have consumer units ...
... that rely on ordinary fuses. In these cases, ...
... it is advisable to use an **ADAPTER PLUG** ...
... which contains a circuit breaker ...
... when using certain appliances ...
... such as a lawnmower or hedge cutter.

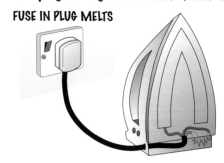

Earthing

All electrical appliances with outer metal cases **MUST BE EARTHED.**
The outer case of the appliance is connected to the **EARTH PIN** in the plug through the **EARTH WIRE** ...

EARTH WIRE ATTACHED TO METAL CASE

FUSE IN PLUG MELTS

- Normally the current flowing ...
- ... is <u>BELOW</u> the current rating ...
- ... of the fuse.
- The appliance (iron) ...
- ... works properly.

However ...
- ... if a fault in the appliance connects the live wire to the case, then the case will become **LIVE!**
- This current will 'run to earth' through the earth wire, because this offers less resistance ...
- ... and this **OVERLOAD** of current will cause the fuse wire to melt (or a circuit breaker to trip).

| 'LIVE' CASING | → | SHORT CIRCUIT | → | CURRENT 'SURGES' TO EARTH | → | FUSE MELTS | → | CIRCUIT BROKEN | → | CABLE OR APPLIANCE IS PROTECTED |

Most of the energy transferred in homes and industry is ELECTRICAL ENERGY because it is easily transferred as ...

... **HEAT** (thermal),   **LIGHT**,   **SOUND**   and **MOVEMENT** (kinetic) energy.

Power Ratings Of Some Domestic Appliances

Most appliances in the home depend on the transfer of ELECTRICAL ENERGY into other FORMS OF ENERGY. All appliances have a POWER RATING which tells us how much ENERGY IS TRANSFERRED by that appliance EVERY SECOND. The rate of energy transfer is measured in WATTS where 1 watt is the transfer of 1 joule of energy in 1 second. The greater the power rating, the more energy is transferred by that appliance EVERY SECOND.
Here are some examples ...

APPLIANCE				
POWER RATING (W)	120 W	600 W	900 W	2000 W
POWER RATING (kW) 1000 watts (W) = 1 Kilowatt (kW)	0.12 kW	0.6 kW	0.9 kW	2 kW
ENERGY TRANSFERRED PER SECOND (J/s)	120 J/s	600 J/s	900 J/s	2000 J/s

Calculating The Energy Transferred By An Electrical Appliance

The energy transferred by an electrical appliance depends on ...
1. How long the appliance is switched on (in seconds).
2. How fast the appliance transfers energy (its POWER in watts)
It is calculated as follows.

ENERGY TRANSFERRED (J) = POWER (W) x TIME (s)

(**REMEMBER!**) POWER in WATTS, TIME in SECONDS ⟶ ENERGY in JOULES

EXAMPLE
An 1800W electric kettle is switched on for 2 min 30 secs. How much electrical energy will the kettle transfer to heat energy while it is switched on?

Using our formula: ENERGY TRANSFERRED = POWER x TIME   (TIME must be in SECONDS remember.)
   = 1800W x 150s
   = 270,000 joules

Calculating The Power Rating Of An Appliance

If we know the energy transferred and time then we can calculate the power rating of an appliance by rearranging the formula above using the formula triangle.

$$POWER (W) = \frac{ENERGY\ TRANSFERRED\ (J)}{TIME\ TAKEN\ (s)}$$

EXAMPLE
A toaster transfers 108,000J of electrical energy into heat in the 120 secs it takes to toast two pieces of bread. Calculate its power rating.

Using our formula: POWER = $\frac{ENERGY\ TRANSFERRED}{TIME\ TAKEN}$ = $\frac{108,000\ J}{120\ s}$ = 900 J/s
   = 900W or 0.9 kW

The Electricity Meter In Your Home

Your meter at home may show a reading like this ...

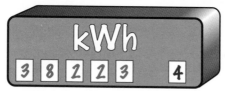

The letters kWh represent ...

... kilowatt-hours, a unit of ENERGY.

These are sometimes called 'Units,' and are a measure of the electrical energy you have used.

1kWh = 3,600,000 joules

Your latest bill may look like this ...

REB Regional **Electricity** Board

Meter readings (E=Estimate C=Your Own)

This time	Last time	Units used	Tariff	Pence per unit (kWh)	Amount £
1957	897E	1060	D9	6.5	68.90

Standing charge this quarter	10.00
Total charges this quarter excluding VAT.	78.90
VAT @ 5.0%	3.95
Total Charges this quarter including VAT.	82.85
BALANCE	**£82.85**

The Kilowatt-hour

The Kilowatt-hour is a unit of ENERGY ...

... please remember it is NOT a unit of power- that's the kilowatt!!

An electrical appliance transfers 1 kWh of energy if it transfers energy at the rate of 1 kilowatt for one hour.

A 200 watt T.V. set   ... transfers 1 kWh of energy if it is switched on for **5** hours.

A 500 watt vacuum cleaner   ... transfers 1 kWh of energy if it is switched on for **2** hours.

A 1,000 watt electric fire   ... transfers 1 kWh of energy if it is switched on for **1** hour.

Kilowatt-hour Calculations

In order to work out the number of kilowatt-hours or 'Units' transferred by an appliance we need the following formula ...

ENERGY TRANSFERRED (kWh) = **POWER** (kW) x **TIME** (h)

EXAMPLE

A 2000 watt electric hot plate is switched on for 90 minutes. How much does it cost if electricity is 6p per unit?

Using our formula: ENERGY TRANSFERRED   = POWER x TIME   *(POWER IN kW; TIME IN HOURS)*

= 2 kW x 1.5h

= 3 kilowatt-hours (or **UNITS**)

But,   TOTAL COST = NUMBER OF UNITS x COST PER UNIT

Therefore Total Cost   = 3 x 6

= 18 pence

And finally, to do these calculations, you must remember ...

... to make sure the POWER is in KILOWATTS, and ...

... to make sure that the TIME is in HOURS.

- TWO MATERIALS can become ELECTRICALLY CHARGED when they are RUBBED AGAINST EACH OTHER.
- The materials have become charged with STATIC ELECTRICITY which means ...
- ... that the electricity stays on the material and doesn't move.

You can 'generate' static electricity by rubbing a balloon against a jumper.

The electrically charged balloon will then attract very small objects.

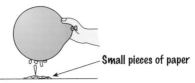

Small pieces of paper

- Electric charge (static) builds up when ELECTRONS (which have a NEGATIVE charge) are 'rubbed off' one material onto another. The material receiving electrons becomes NEGATIVELY CHARGED and the one giving up electrons becomes EQUALLY POSITIVELY CHARGED.

eg. PERSPEX ROD RUBBED WITH A CLOTH

eg. EBONITE ROD RUBBED WITH FUR

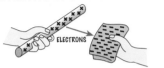

Perspex LOSES electrons ...
... to become ...
... POSITIVELY CHARGED.

Cloth GAINS electrons ...
... to become ...
... NEGATIVELY CHARGED.

Ebonite GAINS electrons ...
... to become ...
... NEGATIVELY CHARGED.

Fur LOSES electrons ...
... to become ...
... POSITIVELY CHARGED.

Repulsion And Attraction Between Charged Materials

Very simply, two materials with ...

... THE SAME CHARGES REPEL EACH OTHER.

... DIFFERENT CHARGES ATTRACT EACH OTHER.

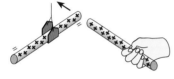

NB
We would get the same with two ebonite rods.

NB
We would get the same if the rods were the other way around.

- The SUSPENDED PERSPEX ROD ...
- ... is REPELLED by the OTHER PERSPEX ROD.

- The SUSPENDED PERSPEX ROD ...
- ... is ATTRACTED by the EBONITE ROD.

Discharge Of Static Electricity

- A charged conductor can be DISCHARGED ie. have any charge on it removed by connecting it to EARTH with a CONDUCTOR.

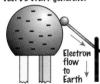

Negatively charged dome of Van De Graff generator

Electron flow to Earth

In this case electrons flow from the dome to Earth via the conductor ... until the dome is completely discharged.

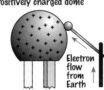

Positively charged dome

Electron flow from Earth

This time the electrons flow from Earth to cancel out the positive charge on the dome ... until the dome is completely discharged.

This flow of electrons through a solid conductor is an ELECTRIC CURRENT and ...

- - - - - - - - HIGHER TIER - - - - - - - -

... metals conduct electricity well because electrons from their atoms can move freely throughout the metal structure. However ...
- ... the GREATER the CHARGE on an ISOLATED OBJECT ...
- ... the GREATER the VOLTAGE (POTENTIAL DIFFERENCE) between the object and Earth.
- If the voltage between the object and a nearby earthed conductor becomes high enough, then ...
- ... this can cause the air molecules to ionise and 'ZAP!', there is a spark as DISCHARGE occurs.

In this case electrons flow from the dome <u>through the air</u> to get to earth via the conductor.

Electron Flow

In this case electrons flow from the earthed conductor <u>through the air</u> to cancel out the positive charge on the dome.

Electron Flow

Using Static In Everyday Life

1. THE PHOTOCOPIER

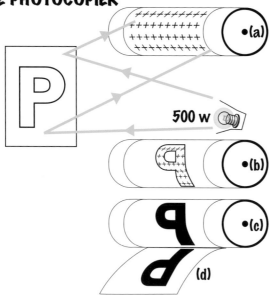

(a) A copying plate is electrically charged (usually positive). An image of the page to be copied is projected onto the plate.

500 w

(b) Light causes charge to leak away leaving an 'electrostatic impression' of the page.

(c) This charged impression of the plate attracts tiny specks of black powder.

(d) This powder is then transferred from the plate to paper which is heated to fix the final image.

2. INKJET PRINTER

Negatively charged ink droplets are squirted between two oppositely charged metal plates across which a variable voltage is applied enabling the charges to be varied and swapped very quickly. The charged droplets of ink are attracted towards the plate with the opposite charge and are therefore deflected to their precise vertical location on the page, while the carriage of the printer moves horizontally across the paper, to give a full range of ink projection.

N.B. This is now old technology but the principle is still important. Also, the system would work just as well with positively charged ink droplets.

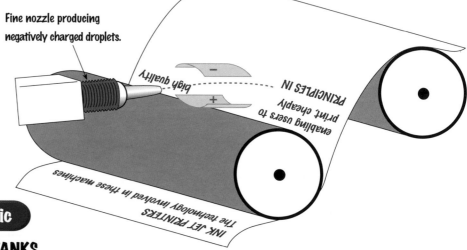

Fine nozzle producing negatively charged droplets.

Discharging Unsafe Static

FILLING AIRCRAFT FUEL TANKS

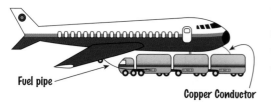

Fuel pipe

Copper Conductor

During refuelling the fuel gains electrons from the fuel pipe, making the pipe positively charged and the fuel negatively charged. The resulting voltage between the two can cause a spark (DISCHARGE). You can imagine the rest!!!

SOLVING THE PROBLEM

Earth the fuel tank with a copper conductor, or ...
... link the tanker and the plane by a copper conductor.
Either of these will allow constant safe discharge to occur.

Speed

One way of describing the movement of an object is by measuring its SPEED, or how fast it is moving.

Since this cyclist travels a DISTANCE of 8 METRES <u>EVERY</u> 1 SECOND we can say that the SPEED of the cyclist is 8m/s.

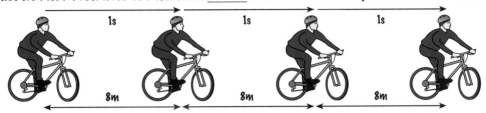

- If we want to work out the SPEED of ANY MOVING OBJECT we need to KNOW TWO THINGS ...

1 The DISTANCE it travels.   **2** The TIME taken to travel that distance.

- We can then calculate the speed of the object using this formula:

$$\text{SPEED (m/s)} = \frac{\text{DISTANCE TRAVELLED (m)}}{\text{TIME TAKEN (s)}}$$

Speed is measured in ... metres per second (m/s), kilometres per hour (km/h) and miles per hour (mph).

EXAMPLE

Calculate the speed of a cyclist who travels 2400m in 5 minutes.

$$\text{SPEED} = \frac{\text{DISTANCE TRAVELLED}}{\text{TIME TAKEN}} = \frac{2400m}{300s} = 8m/s$$

Velocity

Velocity of the car is 40 km/h ...
... EAST.

Velocity of the car is now 40 km/h ...
... SOUTH.

Velocity and speed are not quite the same thing!
The VELOCITY of a moving object is its SPEED IN A GIVEN DIRECTION ...
... ie. you know both the speed <u>and</u> the direction of travel.

Distance-time Graphs

- The slope of a distance-time graph is a measure of the speed of the object ...
- ... and the steeper the slope, the greater the speed.

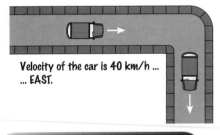

1. Stationary object

2. Object is moving at a constant speed of 2m/s

3. Object is moving at a greater constant speed of 3m/s

Acceleration - Rate Of Change Of Velocity

The acceleration of an object is the rate at which its velocity changes. In other words it is a measure of how quickly an object is speeding up or slowing down.

Since this cyclist INCREASES HIS VELOCITY BY 2 METRES PER SECOND <u>EVERY</u> 1 SECOND ...

... we can say that the ACCELERATION of the cyclist is $2m/s^2$ (2 metres per second, <u>per second</u>).

   1s   1s   1s

0m/s   2m/s   4m/s   6m/s

• If we want to work out the ACCELERATION of ANY MOVING OBJECT we need to know TWO THINGS ...

1 The CHANGE IN VELOCITY   **2** The TIME taken for this change in velocity

• We can then calculate the acceleration or deceleration of the object using this formula:

$$\text{ACCELERATION } (m/s^2) = \frac{\text{CHANGE IN VELOCITY } (m/s)}{\text{TIME TAKEN FOR CHANGE } (s)}$$
(or DECELERATION)

Where v is the final velocity and u is the starting velocity

Acceleration has only ONE unit, metres per second squared, m/s^2.

• There are two important points to be aware of ...

... the cyclist above is increasing his velocity by the SAME AMOUNT EVERY SECOND, however the distance travelled each second is increasing!

... deceleration is simply a negative acceleration. In other words it describes an object which is slowing down.

EXAMPLE

A cyclist accelerates uniformly from rest and reaches a velocity of 10m/s after 5s, before decelerating uniformly and coming to rest in a further 10s. Calculate a) his ACCELERATION, and b) his DECELERATION.

a) $\text{ACC}^N = \dfrac{\text{CHANGE IN VELOCITY}}{\text{TIME TAKEN}} = \dfrac{10 - 0}{5}$

$= 2m/s^2$

b) $\text{DECEL}^N = \dfrac{\text{CHANGE IN VELOCITY}}{\text{TIME TAKEN}} = \dfrac{10 - 0}{10}$

$= 1m/s^2$ ie. a DECELERATION

make sure you state this!!

Velocity-time Graphs

• The slope of a velocity-time graph is a measure of the acceleration of the object ...

• ... and the steeper the slope, the greater the acceleration.

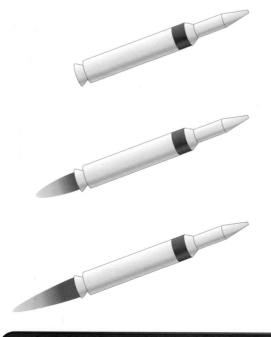

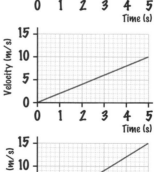

1. Object is moving at a constant speed of 10m/s ie. it is not accelerating at all.

2. Object is moving at a constant acc^n of $2m/s^2$

3. Object is moving at a greater constant acc^n of $3m/s^2$

Distance-time Graphs

The speed of an object can be calculated by working out the gradient of a DISTANCE-TIME GRAPH. The steeper the gradient, the faster the speed. All we have to do is take any point on the graph and read off the DISTANCE travelled at this point, and the TIME taken to get there.

EXAMPLE

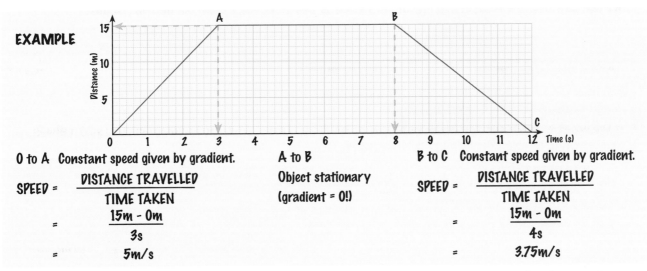

0 to A Constant speed given by gradient.

$$\text{SPEED} = \frac{\text{DISTANCE TRAVELLED}}{\text{TIME TAKEN}}$$

$$= \frac{15m - 0m}{3s}$$

$$= 5m/s$$

A to B

Object stationary
(gradient = 0!)

B to C Constant speed given by gradient.

$$\text{SPEED} = \frac{\text{DISTANCE TRAVELLED}}{\text{TIME TAKEN}}$$

$$= \frac{15m - 0m}{4s}$$

$$= 3.75m/s$$

So in the example above, the object travelled at 5m/s for 3 seconds, remained stationary for 5 secs before returning to its starting point at 3.75m/s for 4 seconds.

Velocity-time Graphs

The acceleration of an object can be calculated by working out the gradient of a VELOCITY-TIME GRAPH. The steeper the gradient, the greater the acceleration. All we have to do is take any point on the graph and read off the CHANGE IN VELOCITY over the chosen period, and the TIME taken for this change.

EXAMPLE

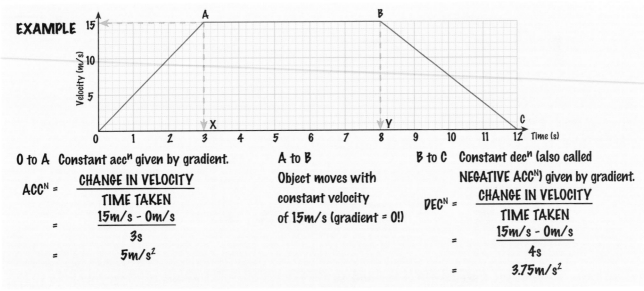

0 to A Constant acc^n given by gradient.

$$\text{ACC}^N = \frac{\text{CHANGE IN VELOCITY}}{\text{TIME TAKEN}}$$

$$= \frac{15m/s - 0m/s}{3s}$$

$$= 5m/s^2$$

A to B

Object moves with
constant velocity
of 15m/s (gradient = 0!)

B to C Constant dec^n (also called
NEGATIVE ACC^N) given by gradient.

$$\text{DEC}^N = \frac{\text{CHANGE IN VELOCITY}}{\text{TIME TAKEN}}$$

$$= \frac{15m/s - 0m/s}{4s}$$

$$= 3.75m/s^2$$

So, in the example above, the object accelerated at 5m/s² for 3 seconds, travelled at a constant speed of 15m/s for 5 secs, before decelerating at a rate of 3.75m/s² for 4 seconds.

- The total distance travelled can be calculated by working out the AREA UNDER THE VELOCITY-TIME GRAPH

Total distance travelled = TOTAL AREA UNDER GRAPH

= Area of OAX + Area of ABYX + Area of BCY

= (½ x 3 x 15) + (5 x 15) + (½ x 4 x 15)

= 22.5 + 75 + 30

= 127.5m

Forces are PUSHES or PULLS eg. FRICTION, WEIGHT, AIR RESISTANCE.
They are measured in NEWTONS (N) and may be different in SIZE and act in different directions.

Forces Acting On An Object At Rest

When an object rests on a surface ...
- ... there is a <u>downward force</u> exerted by the weight of the object, ...
- ... and an <u>upward force</u> exerted by the surface.
- These two forces are EQUAL and OPPOSITE and therefore the object remains at rest.

NB WHENEVER TWO OBJECTS INTERACT ie. ARE IN CONTACT, THEY EXERT EQUAL AND OPPOSITE FORCES ON EACH OTHER.

How Forces Affect Movement

The movement of an object depends on the forces acting.
- If they are <u>EQUAL</u> and <u>OPPOSITE</u> ...
  ... the forces acting are BALANCED.
- If they are <u>NOT EQUAL</u> and <u>OPPOSITE</u> ...
  ... then an UNBALANCED force acts.

...and the object is ...		If the FORCES acting on the object are BALANCED ...	If an UNBALANCED FORCE acts on the object ...
	... STATIONARY ... (not moving)	... then the object will REMAIN STATIONARY.	... then the object will START TO MOVE IN THE DIRECTION OF THE UNBALANCED FORCE.
	... MOVING AT CONSTANT SPEED ...	... then the object will CONTINUE AT THE SAME CONSTANT SPEED IN THE SAME DIRECTION.	... then the object will SPEED UP OR SLOW DOWN.

EXAMPLE

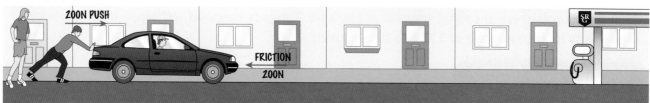

With just one person pushing, THE PUSH FORCE IS EQUAL TO THE FRICTIONAL FORCE, and so the FORCES ARE BALANCED and the STATIONARY CAR <u>REMAINS STATIONARY.</u>

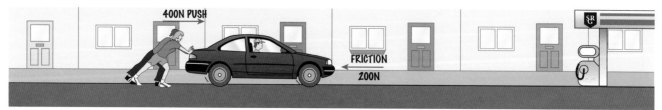

With two people now pushing, THE PUSH FORCE IS GREATER THAN THE FRICTIONAL FORCE, and so an UNBALANCED FORCE acts and the STATIONARY CAR <u>will now START TO MOVE AND SPEED UP (ACCELERATE).</u>

When one person drops out, THE PUSH FORCE IS EQUAL TO THE FRICTIONAL FORCE AGAIN, but these BALANCED FORCES will keep the MOVING CAR moving <u>AT THE SAME CONSTANT SPEED.</u>

With the petrol pump getting nearer, the other person drops out, making the PUSH FORCE LESS THAN THE FRICTIONAL FORCE, and an UNBALANCED FORCE acts. This causes the car to <u>SLOW DOWN (DECELERATE) AND EVENTUALLY STOP.</u>

- A satellite is a smaller object which is in orbit around a much larger object.
- It is kept in this orbit by a combination of ...
  - ... ITS HIGH ORBITING SPEED and ...
  - ... THE FORCE OF GRAVITY BETWEEN THE BODIES.

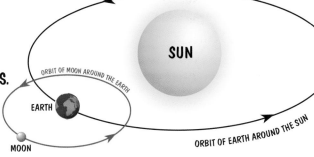

Gravity And Orbiting Speed

As the distance between two bodies <u>increases</u>, there is a proportionally greater <u>decrease</u> in the force of gravity between them ...

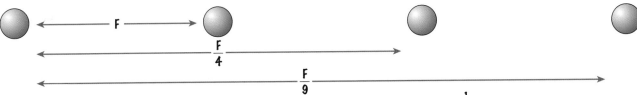

If the distance between two objects is doubled the force between them becomes $\frac{1}{4}$ of the original force. Trebling the distance results in $\frac{1}{9}$ th of the force!

This means that to stay in orbit at a particular distance, smaller bodies must orbit at a particular speed, to balance the gravitational force. For satellites at large distances this means orbiting slowly and therefore taking a much longer time to complete an orbit (due to slow speed and huge circumference of orbit!)

Artificial Satellites

These are placed in orbit by scientists to do a particular job ...

❶ OBSERVATION SATELLITES

- These are in orbit ABOVE THE EARTH'S ATMOSPHERE.
- These have TELESCOPES and the SOLAR SYSTEM and beyond can be OBSERVED without ...
- ... any INTERFERENCE from the ATMOSPHERE, CLOUDS and WEATHER STORMS.

❷ COMMUNICATIONS SATELLITES

- These LINK UP different countries so that ...
- ... RADIO, TV broadcasts and TELEPHONE CALLS ...
- ... can be SENT from ONE COUNTRY TO ANOTHER

❸ MONITORING SATELLITES

- These collect INFORMATION about the ATMOSPHERE ...
- ... including MOVEMENT OF CLOUDS ...
- ... so that WEATHER FORECASTS can be made.

GEOSTATIONARY COMMUNICATIONS SATELLITES

The satellite has an orbit passing high above the equator moving around the Earth at exactly the same rate as the Earth spins ie. it takes 24 hours to complete its orbit. This means that it always stays at the same point above the equator ie. a geostationary orbit. Potential interference with each other's signals means that there is only room for about 400 of these satellites.

POLAR MONITORING SATELLITES

The satellite has a low polar orbit ie. it passes continuously over the North and South poles, so that the Earth spins beneath it. These satellites orbit and scan the Earth several times every day, from a much closer range than a geostationary satellite.

Stars, Galaxies And The Universe

- Our SUN is ONE STAR out of the many millions of stars in OUR GALAXY, THE MILKY WAY.
- The Milky Way is ONE GALAXY out of at least a billion galaxies in the UNIVERSE.

The stars in the night sky stay in fixed patterns (called constellations). Those planets, which are visible to the naked eye, look very much like stars because of the light they reflect. The planets, however, unlike stars, move very slowly across the night sky and therefore change their positions relative to the constellations. Many of these constellations have famous names eg. the plough, because of their shapes.

Formation Of Stars

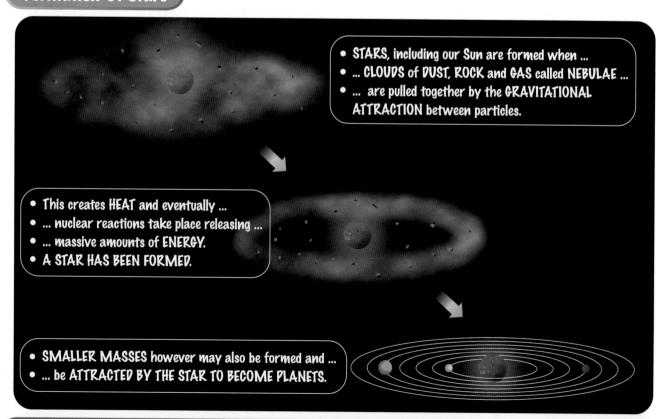

Red Shift

If a SOURCE OF LIGHT (same effect occurs with sound) moves away from us the wavelengths of the light in its spectrum are LONGER than if the source was not moving!!! For light this is known as 'RED-SHIFT' as the wavelengths are 'shifted' TOWARDS THE RED END OF THE SPECTRUM.

The wavelengths of light from other galaxies are longer than expected, which means that ...

... the GALAXY IS MOVING AWAY FROM US VERY QUICKLY ...

... this effect is exaggerated in galaxies which are further away, which means that ...

... the FURTHER AWAY A GALAXY IS, THE FASTER IT IS MOVING AWAY FROM US.

This evidence suggests that the whole universe is expanding and that it might have started billions of years ago, from one place with a 'Big Bang' (a huge explosion!)

BANG!!

How To Detect Life On Other Planets

Amongst the prime contenders for life in our solar system are MARS and EUROPA (one of Jupiter's satellites). However this life may be fairly basic, such as microbes etc. or their fossilised remains.

OBTAINING EVIDENCE

Actually travel to Mars or Europa and look for signs of life!	Use robots to travel to Mars or Europa and bring back samples.	Use robots to travel to Mars or Europa and take pictures!
Could take 18 months to get to Mars though!	Not as reliable as humans!	Pictures might not come out!

ANALYSING EVIDENCE

Looking for fossilised remains ...
The samples you manage to obtain should be sliced carefully using special equipment. The thin slices can then be analysed using an electron microscope.

This principle was applied to a meteorite from Mars which was found in the Antarctic. It revealed some bacteria-like structures!!!

Detecting changes produced by living things ...
The samples of rock or dust can be placed inside a sealed container whose atmosphere has been accurately analysed. Over a period of time the atmosphere is checked to see if there are changes which have occurred

which cannot be attributed to chemical or geological processes eg. oxygen could have been used up or produced by living things in the sample.

SETI

Of course it's possible that there may be highly advanced forms of life elsewhere in the universe and these may be detected using radio telescopes to try to find meaningful signals in a narrow waveband against the background 'noise' of the universe. The SEARCH FOR EXTRA-TERRESTRIAL INTELLIGENCE (SETI) has now gone on for more than 40 years without success; but remember the universe is vast and any day now ...

• During the main stable life period of a star the MASSIVE FORCES of ATTRACTION pulling INWARDS ...
... are BALANCED by FORCES ACTING OUTWARDS created by the HUGE TEMPERATURES within the star.

Towards the end of the star's life, two different processes may occur ...

STAR

... stars at least 4x bigger than our sun can expand enormously to become RED SUPERGIANTS.

... stars the size of our sun will eventually expand to become a RED GIANT.

RED SUPERGIANT

RED GIANT

SUPERNOVA

The RED SUPERGIANT rapidly ...
... SHRINKS and EXPLODES releasing ...
... MASSIVE AMOUNTS OF ENERGY ...
... and DUST and GAS into space.
This is a SUPERNOVA.

WHITE DWARF

The RED GIANT continues to COOL DOWN ...
... and will eventually COLLAPSE under ...
... its own GRAVITY to become a WHITE DWARF ...
... with a density millions of times greater than any matter on Earth.

NEUTRON STAR

For medium-sized stars, (10x bigger than our sun) the remnants of the supernova form a NEUTRON STAR, formed only of neutrons. A cupful of this matter could have a mass greater than 15,000 million tonnes!!

HIGHER TIER

○ **BLACK HOLE**

Those stars greater than 10x the size of our sun are massive enough to leave behind black holes, where the matter is so dense and the gravitational field so strong that nothing can escape from it - not even light or other forms of electromagnetic radiation. Black holes can only be observed indirectly through their effects on their surroundings eg. the X-rays emitted when gases from a nearby star spiral into a black hole.

Recycling Stellar Material

We now know that lighter elements such as hydrogen and helium fuse together to produce NUCLEI of heavier elements during the nuclear fusion reactions which release energy in stars.
But atoms of these heavier elements are also present in the inner planets of the solar system, leading us to believe that the solar system was formed from the material produced when earlier stars exploded.

SPEED AND VELOCITY

$$\text{SPEED (m/s)} = \frac{\text{DISTANCE TRAVELLED (m)}}{\text{TIME TAKEN (s)}}$$

- It can be measured in m/s, km/h or mph.
- VELOCITY is speed in a given direction.
- Speed can be shown on a DISTANCE-TIME graph.

STATIONARY OBJECT   CONSTANT SPEED OF 2m/s   CONSTANT SPEED OF 3m/s

INTERPRETING DISTANCE-TIME GRAPHS

Stationary

5 m/s away from the starting position

3.75 m/s back to the starting position

The GRADIENT (slope) of a distance-time graph gives the SPEED of the object.

ACCELERATION

Acceleration is the 'rate of change of velocity.'

$$\text{ACCELERATION (m/s}^2) = \frac{\text{CHANGE IN VELOCITY (m/s)}}{\text{TIME TAKEN FOR CHANGE (s)}}$$

$$\frac{v-u}{a \times t}$$

It is only measured in metres per second per second (m/s²).
Acceleration can be shown on a VELOCITY-TIME graph.

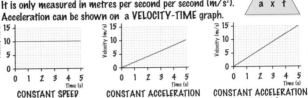

CONSTANT SPEED   CONSTANT ACCELERATION OF 2m/s²   CONSTANT ACCELERATION OF 3m/s²

INTERPRETING VELOCITY-TIME GRAPHS

Constant Speed

Acceleration of 5 m/s²

127.5 m

Deceleration of 3.75 m/s²

The TOTAL AREA under a velocity-time graph represents the DISTANCE TRAVELLED by the object. The gradient gives the acceleration.

FORCE, MASS AND ACCELERATION

When an object rests on a surface ...
- ... there is a <u>downward force</u> exerted by the weight of the object, ...
- ... and an <u>upward force</u> exerted by the surface.
- These two forces are EQUAL and OPPOSITE and therefore the object remains at rest.

... and the object is ...	If the FORCES acting on the object are BALANCED ...	If an UNBALANCED FORCE acts on the object ...
... STATIONARY ... (not moving)	... then the object will REMAIN STATIONARY.	... then the object will START TO MOVE IN THE DIRECTION OF THE UNBALANCED FORCE.
... MOVING AT CONSTANT SPEED ...	... then the object will CONTINUE AT THE SAME CONSTANT SPEED IN THE SAME DIRECTION.	... then the object will SPEED UP OR SLOW DOWN.

- Increasing mass decreases acceleration.
- Increasing force increases acceleration.

$$\text{FORCE (N)} = \text{MASS (kg)} \times \text{ACCELERATION (m/s}^2)$$

ONE NEWTON is the force needed to give a mass of one kilogram an acceleration of one metre per second per second (m/s²).

$$\frac{F}{m \times a}$$

FRICTION, STOPPING DISTANCE AND TERMINAL VELOCITY

Friction opposes the direction of movement of an object through a medium. Friction causes objects to heat up and to wear away.

STOPPING DISTANCE depends on ...
- THE THINKING DISTANCE and
- THE BRAKING DISTANCE

The overall stopping distance can be increased due to
... increased speed, adverse weather conditions, tiredness, drugs and alcohol, poor vehicle condition.

TERMINAL VELOCITY A falling object ...
... experiences acceleration due to gravity ...

... followed by steadily increasing air resistance which causes ...

... a decrease in the RATE OF ACCELERATION until ...

... when R=W he reaches TERMINAL VELOCITY and falls at a constant speed.

THE SOLAR SYSTEM, STARS AND GALAXIES

PLANETS OF THE SOLAR SYSTEM

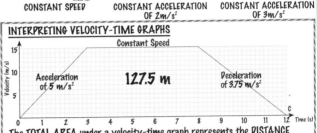

SUN, MERCURY, VENUS, EARTH, MARS, JUPITER, SATURN, URANUS, NEPTUNE, PLUTO

Comets are made of frozen gas and dust and orbit the sun in huge elliptical orbits.
The further away an orbiting body is, the longer it takes to make a complete orbit. The orbit is maintained due to ORBITING SPEED and the FORCE OF GRAVITY.

ARTIFICIAL SATELLITES are used for ...
1. OBSERVATION eg. Hubble Telescope.
2. COMMUNICATION. These are geostationary.
3. MONITORING. These have a low polar orbit.

STARS, GALAXIES AND THE UNIVERSE

Our sun is one star out of millions in our galaxy. Our galaxy (the milky way) is one galaxy out of at least a billion in the universe.
- Stars are formed when clouds of dusts and gas are pulled together by gravitational attraction.

LIFE IN THE UNIVERSE AND THE LIFE CYCLE OF A STAR

RED SHIFT
The wavelengths of light from other galaxies are longer than expected proving that they are moving away from us. This suggests the 'BIG BANG THEORY'.

LIFE ON OTHER PLANETS
Samples of extra-terrestrial material needs to be examined for fossils and also to see if changes occur in the atmosphere above it which could be attributed to life. S.E.T.I. has been trying to detect meaningful radio signals from space for over 40 years without success.

LIFE CYCLE OF A STAR

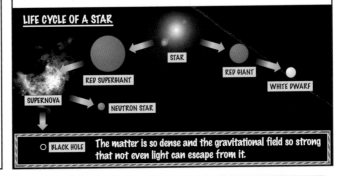

STAR, RED SUPERGIANT, RED GIANT, WHITE DWARF, SUPERNOVA, NEUTRON STAR

BLACK HOLE — The matter is so dense and the gravitational field so strong that not even light can escape from it.

1. a) John can run 300m in 50s. Calculate his average speed.
   b) Peter can run 300m at an average speed of 5m/s. Calculate the time he takes.
   c) If John and Peter were to race against each other over 300m, who would win and by what distance?

2. A car accelerates from rest and reaches a velocity of 15m/s after 5s before coming to rest with a uniform deceleration of $2m/s^2$. Calculate ...
   a) the acceleration of the car.
   b) the time taken by the car to decelerate to rest.

3. The diagram opposite shows the motion of a cyclist on a road.
   a) What was the cyclist doing over the region ...
   (i) AB, (ii) BC, (iii) CD and (iv) DE.
   b) Over which region did the cyclist have the greatest acceleration? Explain your answer.

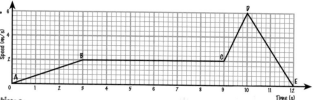

4. The table below shows how the velocity of a car varies with time.

Velocity (m/s)	0	6	12	18	18	18	18	13.5	9	4.5	0
Time (s)	0	10	20	30	40	50	60	70	80	90	100

Draw a graph of velocity on the vertical axis against time on the horizontal axis. From your graph find ...
   a) the acceleration of the car between ...
   (i) 0s and 30s, (ii) 30s and 60s, (iii) 60s and 100s.
   b) the total distance travelled by the car.

5. Copy and complete the table below on how balanced and unbalanced forces affect the movement of an object.

		If the FORCES acting on the object are BALANCED ...	If an UNBALANCED FORCE acts on the object ...
... and the object is ...	... STATIONARY ... (not moving)	... then the object will ----------	... then the object will ---------- ----------
	... MOVING AT CONSTANT SPEED ...	... then the object will ---------- ----------	... then the object will ----------

6. The car opposite is moving along a straight and level road.
   a) What is the name of the force that opposes the movement of the car?
   b) The driver pushes the accelerator pedal down as far as possible.
   Explain in terms of the forces acting on the car why ...
   (i) the car accelerates?
   (ii) the car reaches a maximum speed and cannot accelerate any more?

DIRECTION OF MOTION

7. The moving car above has a mass of 800kg. The maximum forward force that the engine can exert is 4000N. Calculate ...
   a) the acceleration of the car if <u>no</u> frictional force opposes the movement of the car.
   b) the acceleration of the car if a frictional force of 1000N opposes the movement of the car.
   c) the acceleration of the car if a frictional force of 4000N opposes the movement of the car.

8. Which factors affect the stopping distance of a vehicle?

9. a) What is friction?
   b) Give an example of how friction can be undesirable.
   c) Give an example of how friction can be desirable.

10. Describe how the forces acting on a falling body change over the period of time that it is falling.

11. The graph alongside shows the descent of a skydiver from an aeroplane. Explain what is happening at the key points A – E.

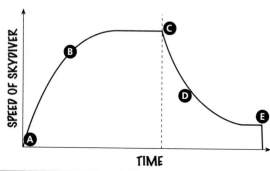

12.

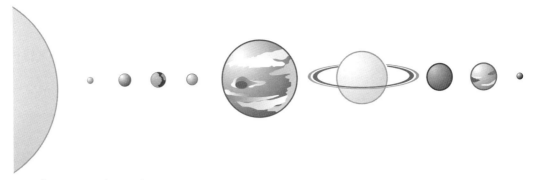

The diagram above shows our solar system.
   a) Which planet would have the longest orbiting time?
   b) Which planet would have the shortest orbiting time?
   c) What is the name given to the shape of the planetary orbits?
   d) Why are we able to see the individual planets?
   e) Why are we able to see individual stars?
   f) What prevents the planets from just drifting off in different directions?

13. a) What is a satellite?
   b) A satellite stays in its orbit due to a combination of two factors. What are they?
   c) Name three natural satellites of the Sun and one natural satellite of the Earth.
   d) What are artificial satellites? Name three uses for them.

14. a) What is a geostationary orbit? Draw a diagram to support your answer.
   b) What is a comet? Draw a diagram to support your answer.
   c) Why do comets become visible as they approach the Sun?

15. a) What is a galaxy?
   b) What can be said about the distance that the stars in a galaxy are apart, compared to the distance that the planets in the solar system are apart?
   c) How are stars formed? Draw a diagram to support your answer.

16. a) During the stable period of a star which two forces are balanced within the star?
   b) Draw flow diagrams to show the two paths a star can follow when it dies.
   c) What evidence is there to support the idea that the solar system was formed from material produced when previous stars exploded?

17. a) The wavelength of a particular colour of light from a distant star in a galaxy is found to have a wavelength longer than expected.
   (i) What is this effect called?
   (ii) What does this prove about the galaxy?
   b) The wavelength of the same particular colour of light from another distant star in another galaxy is found to have an even longer wavelength. What does this prove about the galaxy?

18. a) Describe how it may be possible to bring back samples from a different planet.
   b) Describe the sorts of experiments that may be necessary to show that life exists or existed on that planet.

Waves are ...
- ... a REGULAR PATTERN OF DISTURBANCE ...
- ... which TRANSFERS ENERGY from one point to another WITHOUT ANY TRANSFER OF MATTER.
- Waves can be produced in ROPES, SPRINGS and on the SURFACE OF WATER.

Features Of Waves

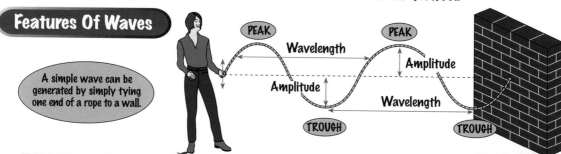

A simple wave can be generated by simply tying one end of a rope to a wall.

AMPLITUDE is ...	WAVELENGTH is ...	FREQUENCY is ...
... the MAXIMUM DISTURBANCE caused by a wave.	... the DISTANCE BETWEEN CORRESPONDING POINTS ON TWO SUCCESSIVE DISTURBANCES.	... the NUMBER of WAVES PRODUCED, (or passing a particular point) IN ONE SECOND.

Types Of Wave

There are TWO types of wave, both of which can be shown using a SLINKY SPRING.

❶ TRANSVERSE WAVES
- The PATTERN OF DISTURBANCE ...
  ... is at RIGHT ANGLES (90°) to ...
  ... the DIRECTION OF WAVE MOVEMENT.

EXAMPLES
- LIGHT which can travel through a vacuum ie. does not need a medium.
- WATERWAVES.
- WAVES IN ROPES.

HAND MOVES UP AND DOWN

DIRECTION OF WAVE MOVEMENT

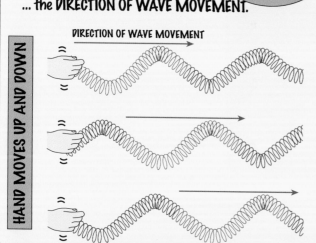

❷ LONGITUDINAL WAVES
- The PATTERN OF DISTURBANCE ...
  ... is in the SAME DIRECTION as ...
  ... the DIRECTION OF WAVE MOVEMENT.

EXAMPLES
- ALL SOUND which can travel through solids, liquids and gases.

HAND MOVES BACKWARDS AND FORWARDS

DIRECTION OF WAVE MOVEMENT

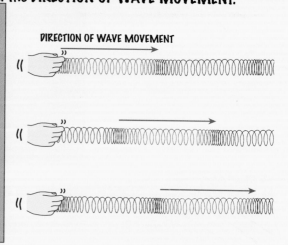

The Wave Equation – Applies To All Waves

For any wave the WAVE SPEED, FREQUENCY and WAVELENGTH are related by the equation:

WAVE SPEED (m/s) = FREQUENCY (Hz) x WAVELENGTH (m)

EXAMPLE 1

A sound wave has a frequency of 165Hz and a wavelength of 2m, what is the speed of sound?
Using our equation: Wave speed = Frequency x Wavelength

$$v = 165Hz \times 2m = \underline{330m/s}$$

EXAMPLE 2

Radio 5 Live transmits from London on a frequency of 909 kHz. If the speed of radio waves is 300,000,000m/s, what is the wavelength of the waves?

Using our equation:
(now rearranged)   Wavelength = $\dfrac{\text{Wave speed}}{\text{Frequency}}$ $\lambda = \dfrac{300,000,000m/s}{909,000Hz} = \underline{330m}$

Reflection Of Waves

- Waves are REFLECTED when a BARRIER is placed in their path.
- The effect can be seen with waves generated ...
- ... in a ROPE or SPRING ...
- ... and with WATERWAVES.

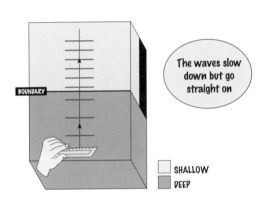

Refraction Of Waves

- When WAVES CROSS A BOUNDARY ...
- ... between ONE MEDIUM AND ANOTHER (OF DIFFERENT DENSITY) ...
- ... there is a CHANGE OF SPEED of the waves ...
- ... which causes the waves to CHANGE DIRECTION ...
- ... unless the waves meet the boundary along a NORMAL (AT 90°).
- With WATERWAVES refraction occurs when the waves pass into DEEPER or SHALLOWER WATER.

WATERWAVES PASSING INTO SHALLOWER WATER

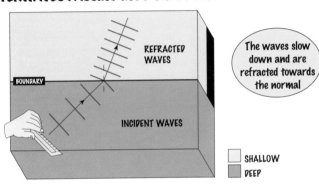

WATERWAVES PASSING INTO DEEPER WATER

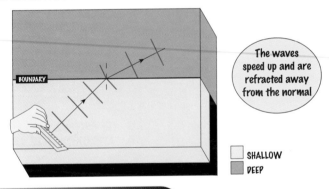

Diffraction Of Waves

- When WAVES MOVE THROUGH A GAP or PAST AN OBSTACLE ...
- ... they SPREAD OUT FROM THE EDGES. This is DIFFRACTION.

Diffraction is most obvious when:

| 1. THE SIZE OF THE GAP IS SIMILAR TO THE WAVELENGTH OF THE WAVES. | 2. THE WAVES WHICH PASS OBSTACLES HAVE LONG WAVELENGTHS. |

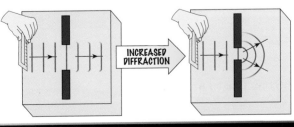

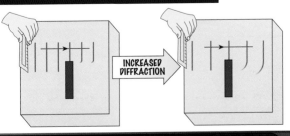

The behaviour of waves shown on the previous page suggests that light and sound (see p.43) also travel as waves and are refracted because they travel at different speeds in different materials (media).

Reflection Of Light

This occurs when light strikes a SURFACE resulting in it CHANGING ITS DIRECTION. If the surface is perfectly smooth and shiny (eg. a mirror) then the following law of reflection applies ...

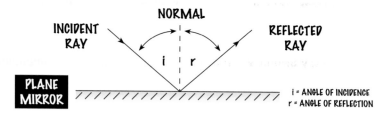

i = ANGLE OF INCIDENCE
r = ANGLE OF REFLECTION

ANGLE OF INCIDENCE = ANGLE OF REFLECTION

Refraction Of Light

Light changes direction when it crosses a boundary between two transparent materials (media) of different densities - UNLESS it meets the boundary at an angle of 90° (along a NORMAL).

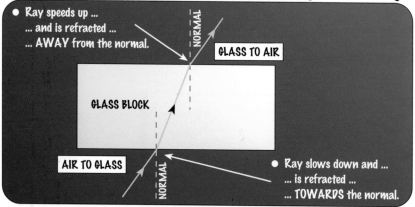

- Ray speeds up ...
  ... and is refracted ...
  ... AWAY from the normal.

GLASS TO AIR

GLASS BLOCK

AIR TO GLASS

- Ray slows down and ...
  ... is refracted ...
  ... TOWARDS the normal.

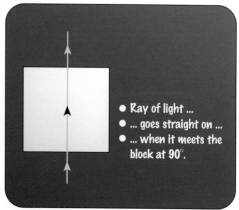

- Ray of light ...
- ... goes straight on ...
- ... when it meets the block at 90°.

Total Internal Reflection – When Refraction Becomes Reflection

When a ray of light travels from glass, 'perspex' or water into air, some light is also reflected from the boundary. This can be best summarised in THREE stages. If the ANGLE OF INCIDENCE is ...

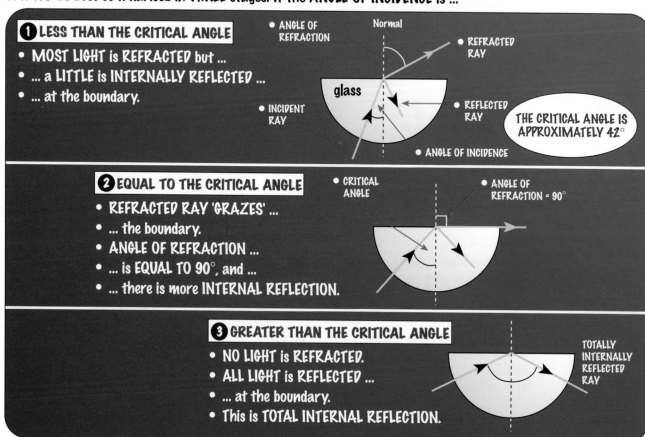

❶ LESS THAN THE CRITICAL ANGLE

- MOST LIGHT is REFRACTED but ...
- ... a LITTLE is INTERNALLY REFLECTED ...
- ... at the boundary.

● ANGLE OF REFRACTION
Normal
● REFRACTED RAY
glass
● INCIDENT RAY
● REFLECTED RAY
● ANGLE OF INCIDENCE

THE CRITICAL ANGLE IS APPROXIMATELY 42°

❷ EQUAL TO THE CRITICAL ANGLE

- REFRACTED RAY 'GRAZES' ...
- ... the boundary.
- ANGLE OF REFRACTION ...
- ... is EQUAL TO 90°, and ...
- ... there is more INTERNAL REFLECTION.

● CRITICAL ANGLE
● ANGLE OF REFRACTION = 90°

❸ GREATER THAN THE CRITICAL ANGLE

- NO LIGHT is REFRACTED.
- ALL LIGHT is REFLECTED ...
- ... at the boundary.
- This is TOTAL INTERNAL REFLECTION.

TOTALLY INTERNALLY REFLECTED RAY

1. Optical Fibres

An OPTICAL FIBRE is ...
- ... a LONG, FLEXIBLE, TRANSPARENT CABLE ...
- ... of very SMALL DIAMETER.

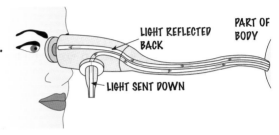

ALL ANGLES OF INCIDENCE INSIDE THE ROD ARE GREATER THAN THE CRITICAL ANGLE.

As light travels down an optical fibre ...
- ... it is TOTALLY INTERNALLY REFLECTED ...
- ... REPEATEDLY ALONG ITS LENGTH, ...
- ... staying inside the fibre ...
- ... until it emerges from the other end.

EXAMPLES

❶ THE ENDOSCOPE

- Used for INTERNAL VIEWING OF THE HUMAN BODY.
- The endoscope consists of BUNDLES OF FIBRES, half of which ...
- ... TRANSMIT LIGHT to the part of the body being VIEWED ...
- ... and half of them TRANSMIT REFLECTED LIGHT BACK ...
- ... to form an IMAGE.

LIGHT REFLECTED BACK   PART OF BODY

LIGHT SENT DOWN

❷ TELECOMMUNICATIONS

- Information can be TRANSMITTED via PULSES of light travelling along OPTICAL FIBRES.
- MORE information can be sent this way than by sending ELECTRICAL SIGNALS ...
- ... through CABLES of the SAME DIAMETER ...
- ... with LESS WEAKENING of SIGNAL STRENGTH along the way.

2. Reflecting Prisms

These can be used to REFLECT LIGHT through ...

... 90°   ... 180°

45°
45°
45°

ALL ANGLES OF INCIDENCE INSIDE THE PRISMS ARE 45° ie. GREATER THAN THE CRITICAL ANGLE.

45°

EXAMPLES

❶ PERISCOPE

- TWO PRISMS needed.
- ALL LIGHT is REFLECTED.
- Better than a ...
  ... MIRROR PERISCOPE ...
  ... as some light is absorbed.

❷ PRISM BINOCULARS

- Contains FOUR PRISMS ...
  ... whose job is to ...
  ... produce a FINAL ...
  ... UPRIGHT IMAGE ...
  ... for the user.

❸ BICYCLE REFLECTORS AND CAT'S EYES

- These REFLECT LIGHT ...
  ... BACK in the direction ...
  ... it came from.

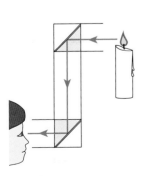

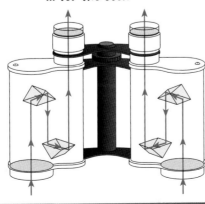

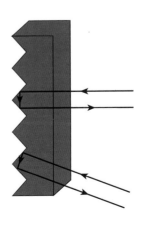

Light is one type of ELECTROMAGNETIC RADIATION, which together with the other various types form a continuous range called the ELECTROMAGNETIC SPECTRUM. The seven 'colours of the rainbow' form the visible spectrum, which as the name suggests is the only part of the electromagnetic spectrum that we can see. Electromagnetic radiation can be REFLECTED, REFRACTED and DIFFRACTED which supports the idea that they travel as WAVES.

Types Of Electromagnetic Radiation In The Electromagnetic Spectrum

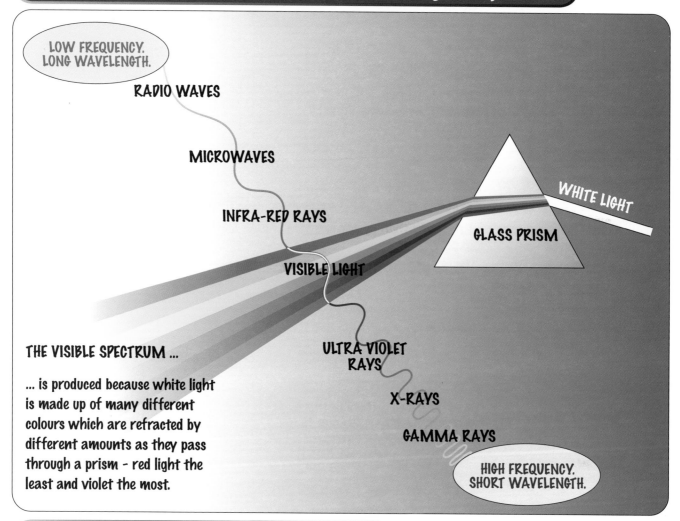

LOW FREQUENCY. LONG WAVELENGTH.

RADIO WAVES

MICROWAVES

INFRA-RED RAYS

VISIBLE LIGHT

WHITE LIGHT

GLASS PRISM

THE VISIBLE SPECTRUM ...

... is produced because white light is made up of many different colours which are refracted by different amounts as they pass through a prism - red light the least and violet the most.

ULTRA VIOLET RAYS

X-RAYS

GAMMA RAYS

HIGH FREQUENCY. SHORT WAVELENGTH.

Characteristics Of Electromagnetic Radiation

• Each type of electromagnetic radiation ...
1. TRAVELS AT THE SAME SPEED (300,000,000m/s) THROUGH SPACE (a vacuum).
2. Has a DIFFERENT WAVELENGTH and a DIFFERENT FREQUENCY.

RADIO WAVES, MICROWAVES and INFRA-RED RAYS <u>ALL</u> have a LONGER WAVELENGTH and a LOWER FREQUENCY compared to VISIBLE LIGHT.	ULTRA VIOLET RAYS, X-RAYS and GAMMA RAYS <u>ALL</u> have a SHORTER WAVELENGTH and a HIGHER FREQUENCY compared to VISIBLE LIGHT.

• Different wavelengths of electromagnetic radiation are REFLECTED, ABSORBED, or TRANSMITTED DIFFERENTLY by DIFFERENT SUBSTANCES and TYPE OF SURFACE eg. Black surfaces are particularly good absorbers of infra-red radiation.

5mins later

• When radiation is absorbed, the energy it carries ...
  ... MAKES THE SUBSTANCE WHICH ABSORBS IT HOTTER, ...
  ... MAY CREATE AN ALTERNATING CURRENT WITH THE SAME FREQUENCY AS THE RADIATION.
This principle is used in TV and radio aerials to receive information via radio waves.

Uses Of Electromagnetic Waves

Effects Of Electromagnetic Waves

RADIO WAVES

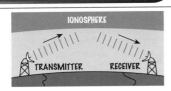

- Transmit Radio and TV programmes between different places. The longer wavelength radio waves are reflected ...
  ... from the ionosphere, an electrically charged layer ...
  ... in the Earth's upper atmosphere.

- This means that long wave radio waves can be sent between different points despite the fact that the Earth's surface curves.

MICROWAVES

- Satellite communication and mobile phone networks since they can pass easily through the Earth's atmosphere.

- Cooking, because microwaves are ...
- ... absorbed by water molecules ...
- ... causing them to heat up.

- Microwaves are dangerous because they are absorbed by water in cells ...
  ... where the heat released ...
  ... may DAMAGE or KILL CELLS.
Correct care must be taken in the use of microwaves.

INFRA-RED RAYS

- Grills, toasters and radiant heaters.
- Remote control for TV ...
  ... and VCR's.
- Optical Fibre communication.

- Absorbed by skin ...
  ... and FELT as HEAT.
Excessive amount can cause BURNS.

VISIBLE SPECTRUM (see P.40)

ULTRA VIOLET RAYS

- For suntanning and sunbeds.

- Fluorescent lamp & security coding ...
  ... where surface coated with special paint ...
  ... absorbs U-V and emits visible LIGHT.

- Passes through skin to the TISSUES below. Darker skin allows less penetration ...
  ... and provides more protection.
- HIGH DOSES of this ionising radiation can KILL NORMAL CELLS ...
  ... and a LOW DOSE can cause CANCER.

X-RAYS

- Produce shadow pictures of ...
  ... BONES and METALS, ...
  ... materials X-rays do not easily pass through.

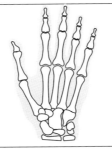

- Pass through SOFT TISSUES ...
  ... although SOME is ABSORBED.
- As for U-V ...
  ... HIGH DOSES of this ionising radiation can KILL NORMAL CELLS ...
  ... and LOW DOSES can cause CANCER.

GAMMA RAYS

- Killing cancer cells.

- Killing bacteria on food ...
  ... and surgical instruments.

- Pass through SOFT TISSUES ...
  ... although SOME is ABSORBED.
- As for U-V and X-Rays ...
  ... HIGH DOSES of this ionising radiation can KILL NORMAL CELLS ...
  ... and LOW DOSES can cause CANCER.

Sound eg. speech or music can be sent long distances if it is converted into electrical signals ...

A microphone in the mouthpiece converts sound into electrical signals which pass down the wire. These electrical signals match the frequency and amplitude of the sound waves.

These electrical signals can then be sent using ...

... CABLES.
Copper cables suffer from weakening of the signal during transmission.
To boost the signal regular amplification of the signal is required.

... ELECTROMAGNETIC WAVES.
Here a radio wave is used to 'carry' the electrical signal from a transmitter ...

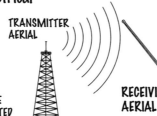

SIGNAL + CARRIER ⇒ MODULATED WAVE WHICH IS TRANSMITTED

TRANSMITTER AERIAL

RECEIVING AERIAL

... the modulated wave is then demodulated by a receiver back into the signal.

MODULATED WAVE

SIGNAL

| TUNER | → | DEMODULATOR | → | LOUDSPEAKER |

Optical Fibres

Information can also be transmitted using OPTICAL FIBRES where the electrical signal is converted into light or infra red pulses.

More information can be sent this way than by sending electrical signals through cables of the same diameter, with less weakening of signal strength along the way.

Analogue And Digital Signals

- Analogue signals vary continually in amplitude and/or frequency. They are very similar to the sound waves of speech or music.

- Digital signals on the other hand do not vary and they have only two states, ON (I) or OFF (0). There are no inbetween states. The information is a series of pulses.

+ / − TIME

I / 0 TIME

The advantages of using digital signals instead of analogue signals are ...
- ... better quality, with no change in the signal information during transmission.
- ... more information can be transmitted in a given time via cable, optical fibre or carrier wave.

――――――――――――――――― HIGHER TIER ―――――――

Why Digital Is Better Than Analogue

Transmitted signals become weaker. They may also pick up additional signals or noise. At selective intervals the transmitted signals have to be amplified.
- Different frequencies within analogue signals weaken by different amounts. When amplified these differences and any noise which has been picked up results in the signal becoming less and less like the original signal ie. there is a deterioration in quality.
- Digital signals also weaken during transmission. However, the pulses are still recognisable as 'ON' or 'OFF'. Noise doesn't affect digital signals since it usually has a low amplitude which is recognised as an 'OFF' state. When amplified the quality of the digital signal is retained.

TRANSMITTED SIGNAL ⇒ DETERIORATED SIGNAL ⇒ AMPLIFIED SIGNAL

SOUND ...
- is produced when something VIBRATES backwards and forwards.
- It is REFLECTED from HARD SURFACES, these reflections are called ECHOES and ...
- ... is REFRACTED when it passes into a DIFFERENT MEDIUM or SUBSTANCE.

Since sound can be reflected and refracted this provides evidence that SOUND TRAVELS AS WAVES.

Also, the idea of sound travelling as a wave is supported by the fact that sound can be DIFFRACTED (see P.37) around buildings or land masses. A person in the 'shadow' of a large building can still hear sounds which he would perhaps expect to be 'blocked'.

SOUND WAVES ARE DIFFRACTED BY HOUSE - AEROPLANE CAN BE HEARD.

SOUND WAVES FROM AEROPLANE

Representing Sound On An Oscilloscope Trace

It is possible for us to 'see' a representation of a sound wave if we connect a signal generator to an oscilloscope

A SIGNAL GENERATOR can generate sound waves whose PITCH and LOUDNESS can be changed.

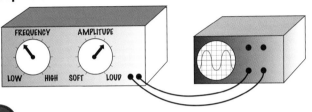

The OSCILLOSCOPE displays a representation of the sound wave on its screen, as a trace.

Frequency And Pitch

The FREQUENCY is the NUMBER OF VIBRATIONS PRODUCED in ONE SECOND. It is measured in HERTZ, Hz. The HIGHER the FREQUENCY of the sound waves, the HIGHER the PITCH of the sound. A change in frequency can be represented on the oscilloscope screen, if the frequency dial of the signal generator is turned.

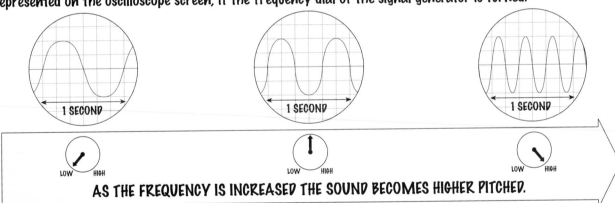

AS THE FREQUENCY IS INCREASED THE SOUND BECOMES HIGHER PITCHED.

Amplitude And Loudness

AMPLITUDE is the BIGGEST MOVEMENT OF THE VIBRATING OBJECT FROM ITS REST POSITION.
The GREATER the AMPLITUDE of the sound waves the GREATER the LOUDNESS of the sound. A change in amplitude can be represented on the oscilloscope screen if the amplitude dial on the signal generator is turned.

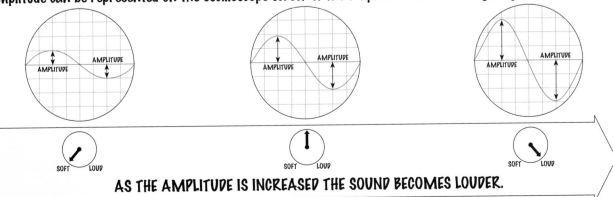

AS THE AMPLITUDE IS INCREASED THE SOUND BECOMES LOUDER.

These are SOUND WAVES of FREQUENCIES GREATER than 20,000 Hz ie. above the UPPER LIMIT of the HEARING RANGE for HUMANS. They are made by ELECTRONIC SYSTEMS which produce ELECTRICAL OSCILLATIONS which are used to generate the ULTRASONIC WAVES.

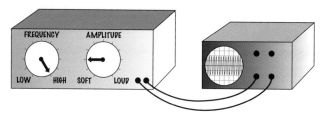

They have many uses ...

1. Pre-natal Scanning

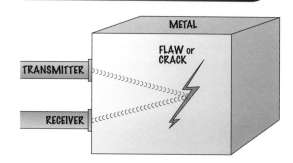

THIS METHOD IS SAFE WITH NO RISK TO PATIENT OR BABY.

2. Detecting Flaws And Cracks

3. Cleaning Delicate Objects

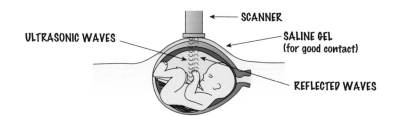

- Some of the ultrasound waves are reflected back by the flaw or crack within the structure.

- The vibrations caused by the ultrasound waves dislodge dirt particles from the surface of the object.

HIGHER TIER

HOW THEY WORK

- Ultrasonic waves are PARTLY REFLECTED ...
- ... at the BOUNDARY as they pass from ...
- ... ONE MEDIUM or SUBSTANCE into another one.
- The TIME TAKEN for these REFLECTIONS is a ...
- ... measure of the DEPTH of the REFLECTING SURFACE and ...
- ... the reflected waves are usually PROCESSED ...
- ... to produce a VISUAL IMAGE on a SCREEN.

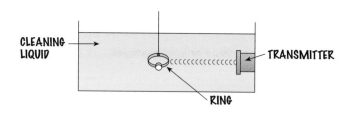

- Ultrasonic waves can also be used within a LIQUID to CLEAN DELICATE OBJECTS where ...
- ... the VIBRATIONS DISLODGE DIRT PARTICLES ...
- ... from the SURFACE of the object.
- Using this method means there is ...
- ... NO DANGER OF BREAKAGE or ...
- ... need to DISASSEMBLE the object.

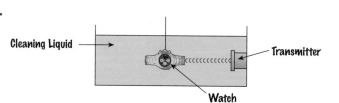

Structure Of The Earth

A THIN CRUST
- Up to 10km thick under oceans.
- Up to 100km thick under continents.

A VISCOUS MANTLE
- SEMI-FLUID whose DENSITY INCREASES ... WITH DEPTH.
- It extends almost HALFWAY TO THE CENTRE.

A CORE
- Over HALF of the Earth's DIAMETER with a ... ... LIQUID OUTER PART and a SOLID INNER PART.

- The overall density of the Earth is much greater than the mean densities of the rocks which form the crust. This indicates that the interior of the Earth is made of different materials, which are denser, than the materials which form the crust.

⟋ HIGHER TIER ⟍

Evidence For The Structure

Evidence for the LAYERED STRUCTURE has been gained by the study of EARTHQUAKES. These are due to the fracture of large masses of rock inside the Earth. The ENERGY which is released TRAVELS through the earth as a series of SHOCK WAVES called SEISMIC WAVES which are detected using SEISMOGRAPHS.
There are two types of shock waves ...

P WAVES
- LONGITUDINAL WAVES where the ground is made to VIBRATE in the SAME DIRECTION as the shock wave is travelling ... ... ie. UP and DOWN.
- PASS THROUGH SOLIDS AND LIQUIDS.
- FASTER THAN S WAVES.
- SPEED INCREASES IN ... ... MORE DENSE MATERIAL.
ie. as they pass deeper into the mantle.

P WAVES
BUILDING VIBRATES
UP AND DOWN

S WAVES
- TRANSVERSE WAVES where the ground is made to VIBRATE at RIGHT ANGLES to the DIRECTION the shock wave is travelling ... ... ie. from LEFT to RIGHT.
- PASS THROUGH SOLIDS ONLY.
- SLOWER THAN P WAVES
- SPEED INCREASES IN ... ... MORE DENSE MATERIAL.
ie. as they pass deeper into the mantle.

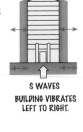

S WAVES
BUILDING VIBRATES
LEFT TO RIGHT.

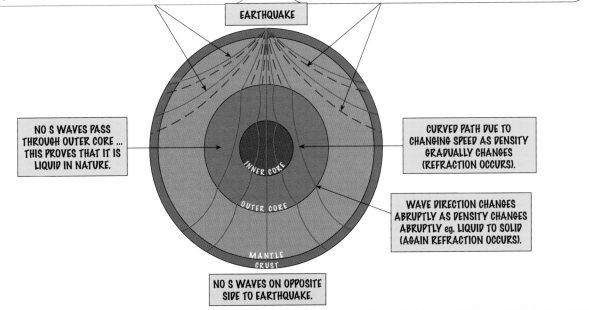

EARTHQUAKE

NO S WAVES PASS THROUGH OUTER CORE ... THIS PROVES THAT IT IS LIQUID IN NATURE.

CURVED PATH DUE TO CHANGING SPEED AS DENSITY GRADUALLY CHANGES (REFRACTION OCCURS).

WAVE DIRECTION CHANGES ABRUPTLY AS DENSITY CHANGES ABRUPTLY eg. LIQUID TO SOLID (AGAIN REFRACTION OCCURS).

INNER CORE

OUTER CORE

MANTLE
CRUST

NO S WAVES ON OPPOSITE SIDE TO EARTHQUAKE.

Movement Of The Lithosphere

The Earth's LITHOSPHERE ie. the CRUST and the UPPER PART OF THE MANTLE ...
... is 'cracked' into several large pieces called TECTONIC PLATES.
These plates move slowly, at speeds of a few cm per year, ...
... driven by CONVECTION CURRENTS in the MANTLE, ...
... which are caused by HEAT released by RADIOACTIVE DECAY.

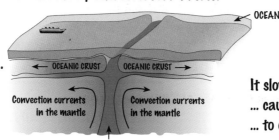

Hot molten rock comes ...
.. up to the surface ...
... at the boundary ...
... between the plates.

It slowly spreads sideways ...
... causing the plates ...
... to gradually move apart.

EARTHQUAKES and VOLCANIC ERUPTIONS are common occurrences at the boundary between two plates. As yet, scientists cannot predict when these events will occur due to the difficulty in taking appropriate measurements. They do, however, know the places where these events are most likely to occur.

The Evidence

At one time people used to believe that the features of the Earth's surface were caused by SHRINKAGE when the Earth cooled, following its formation.
Today, this is rejected in favour of the TECTONIC THEORY ...
Evidence has been gained by comparing the EAST COAST of SOUTH AMERICA and the WEST COAST of AFRICA.
Although separated by thousands of kilometres of ocean, they have ...

1 Closely Matching Shapes

Geologists have long noticed that their coastlines are closely matched and were, therefore, once joined together.

HOW IT ONCE WAS

HOW IT IS TODAY

2 Similar Patterns Of Rocks And Fossils

The East coast of South America and the West coast of Africa have similar patterns of rocks and contain fossils of the same plants and animals eg. the MESOSAURUS.

The Theory

The evidence above led Alfred Wegener to propose that ...
... MOVEMENT OF THE CRUST or CONTINENTAL DRIFT was responsible for their separation ...
... and indeed that they had at one time both been part of a single land mass.
Unfortunately Wegener was unable to explain how the crust moved ...
... and it took more than 50 years for scientists to realise ...
... that the enormous heat released during radioactive decay inside the Earth ...
... generates convection currents in the mantle, causing movement of the crust.
... and the movement of the continents from how they were (as GONDWANALAND and LAURASIA) to what they look like today.

Three Things That Can Happen

The 'plates' on the previous page can basically only do THREE things:

1 Slide Past Each Other

When plates SLIDE, HUGE STRESSES AND STRAINS build up in the crust ...
... which eventually have to be RELEASED in order for MOVEMENT to occur.
This 'release' of energy results in an EARTHQUAKE. A classic example of
this is the West Coast of North America (esp. California).

2 Move Away From Each Other – Constructive Plate Margins

When plates MOVE AWAY FROM EACH OTHER, at an oceanic ridge, FRACTURES OCCUR, ...
... these are filled by MAGMA to produce NEW BASALTIC OCEAN CRUST, ...
... at a rate of 2cm per year.
This is known as SEA FLOOR SPREADING.

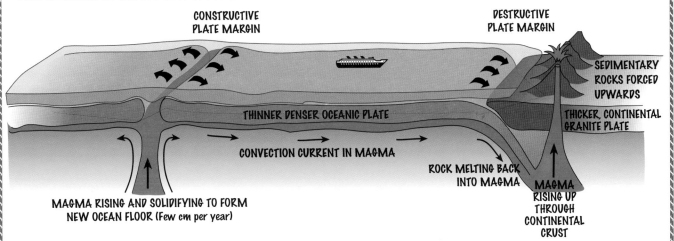

CONSTRUCTIVE PLATE MARGIN

DESTRUCTIVE PLATE MARGIN

SEDIMENTARY ROCKS FORCED UPWARDS

THINNER DENSER OCEANIC PLATE

THICKER, CONTINENTAL GRANITE PLATE

CONVECTION CURRENT IN MAGMA

ROCK MELTING BACK INTO MAGMA

MAGMA RISING UP THROUGH CONTINENTAL CRUST

MAGMA RISING AND SOLIDIFYING TO FORM NEW OCEAN FLOOR (Few cm per year)

3 Move Towards Each Other – Destructive Plate Margins

As plates are moving away from each other in some places ...
... it follows that they must be MOVING TOWARDS EACH OTHER in other places.
This always results in the THINNER, DENSER, OCEANIC PLATE being FORCED DOWN (SUBDUCTED) beneath ...
... the THICKER CONTINENTAL GRANITE PLATE, where it partially MELTS.
This subduction forces continental crust to be compressed resulting in folding and metamorphism.
EARTHQUAKES are common and even VOLCANOES are formed ...
... due to magma rising up through the continental crust eg. West Coast of South America (Andes).

Evidence For Sea Floor Spreading

As Magma rises and solidifies, to form new Basaltic Ocean Crust, ...
... IRON-RICH minerals ORIENTATE themselves in the DIRECTION OF THE EARTH'S MAGNETIC FIELD, ...
... forming MAGNETIC REVERSAL PATTERNS parallel to the OCEANIC RIDGE ...
The magnetic field of the Earth has changed NINE times in the last 3.6 million years, and ...
... this is 'mirrored' in these REVERSAL PATTERNS.

MAGMA RISING   MAGMA RISING   MAGMA RISING

CHARACTERISTICS OF WAVES

FEATURES OF WAVES ... may be <u>transverse</u> eg. light or <u>longitudinal</u> eg. sound.

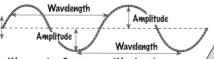

$$\dfrac{v}{f \times \lambda}$$

• Wavespeed = Frequency x Wavelength

REFLECTION, REFRACTION and DIFFRACTION

Waves are reflected when a barrier is placed in their path, and refracted when they pass from one medium into another because they change speed.

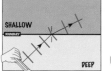 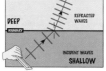

Waves are DIFFRACTED especially when they have long wavelengths or the gap is similar to the wavelength of the waves.

LIGHT AND TOTAL INTERNAL REFLECTION

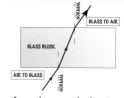

• Angle of incidence = Angle of reflection

Critical Angle

• Light is refracted away from the normal when it passes from glass into air.
• Light is refracted towards the normal when it passes from air into glass.

• If the angle of incidence is greater than the CRITICAL ANGLE then TOTAL INTERNAL REFLECTION occurs.

• Optical fibre - light is totally internally reflected along its length.

• Reflecting prisms - can be used to reflect light through 90° or 180°. eg. Binoculars, periscopes and cats eyes.

ELECTROMAGNETIC WAVES

LOW FREQUENCY.
LONG WAVELENGTH.

RADIO WAVES - creates an alternating current in aerials and can be bounced off the IONOSPHERE.

All types travel at the same speed (300,000,000 m/s) through a vacuum.

MICROWAVES - Satellite communication, mobile phones, microwave ovens. Can damage cells.

INFRA-RED RAYS - Optical fibre communications, TV remotes, and radiant heaters.

VISIBLE LIGHT

The different types have different wavelengths and frequencies.

Security coding and sun lamps. - ULTRA VIOLET RAYS
Can cause skin cancer.

Used to diagnose medical conditions. - X-RAYS
Dangerous to cells.

Used in cancer treatment and for - GAMMA RAYS
sterilisation of surgical equipment.

HIGH FREQUENCY.
SHORT WAVELENGTH.

INFORMATION TRANSMISSION AND SOUND

Sound can be converted into electrical signals and sent through cables or by using electromagnetic waves.
• The signals which vary continually are called ANALOGUE.
• The signals which only exist as ON or OFF are called DIGITAL.
There is less distortion and greater capacity with digital.

All signals weaken with distance but ON and OFF states are still recognisable with digital signals. 'Noise' is recognised as being in the 'OFF state'.

ANALOGUE

DIGITAL

FREQUENCY AND PITCH OF SOUND

LOW FREQUENCY   MID FREQUENCY   HIGH FREQUENCY

AMPLITUDE AND LOUDNESS OF SOUND

QUIET SOUND   LOUDER SOUND   EVEN LOUDER SOUND

ULTRASOUND AND SEISMIC WAVES

ULTRASOUND
Frequencies greater than 20,000Hz.
Used for prenatal scanning, detecting cracks in structures, and cleaning delicate objects.

Work on the principle of part reflection from the boundaries between different media.

EARTH STRUCTURE

CRUST
MANTLE
CORE

SEISMIC WAVES

P WAVES	S WAVES
• LONGITUDINAL WAVES where the ground is made to VIBRATE in the <u>SAME DIRECTION</u> as the shock wave is travelling ... ... ie. UP and DOWN.	• TRANSVERSE WAVES where the ground is made to VIBRATE at <u>RIGHT ANGLES</u> to the DIRECTION the shock wave is travelling ... ... ie. from LEFT to RIGHT.
• PASS THROUGH SOLIDS <u>AND</u> LIQUIDS.	• PASS THROUGH SOLIDS <u>ONLY</u>.
• FASTER THAN S WAVES.	• SLOWER THAN P WAVES
• SPEED INCREASES IN ... ... MORE DENSE MATERIAL. ie. as they pass deeper into the mantle.	• SPEED INCREASES IN ... ... MORE DENSE MATERIAL. ie. as they pass deeper into the mantle.

TECTONIC ACTIVITY

• The earth's lithosphere is cracked into pieces called TECTONIC PLATES, which move slowly driven by convection currents caused by RADIOACTIVE DECAY.

THE EVIDENCE ... for tectonic theory is based on
(a) Closely matching shapes of South America and Africa.
(b) Similar patterns of rocks and fossils near the coasts of the two continents.
(c) Sea floor spreading confirmed by magnetic reversal patterns.
Wegener's theory was only accepted 50 years after it was proposed.

THE EFFECTS ... tectonic plates can ...
(a) Slide past each other causing EARTHQUAKES eg. Coast of California.
(b) Move away from each other - constructive plate margins. The fractures are filled by magma producing new basaltic ocean crust along the oceanic ridges.

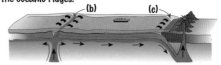

(c) Move towards each other - destructive plate margins. The thinner, denser oceanic plate is SUBDUCTED beneath the thicker continental granite plate into the magma. Mountains and volcanoes may be formed here and folding and metamorphism are common eg. the Andes

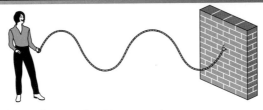

1. a) What is a wave?

   b) (i) What is amplitude? Label it on the diagram above.
   (ii) What is wavelength? Label it on the diagram above.
   (iii) If the frequency of a wave is 10Hz, what does this mean?

2. a) (i) What is a transverse wave?
   (ii) Give two examples.
   b) (i) What is a longitudinal wave?
   (ii) Give two examples.

3. a) A sound wave of frequency 80Hz has a wavelength of 4m. Calculate the speed of sound.
   b) A radiowave has a wavelength of 2km. If the speed of radiowaves is 300,000,000m/s, calculate the frequency of the radiowave.

4. a) Draw a fully labelled diagram to show the reflection of light by a mirror.

5. a) What is refraction?
   b) Draw a diagram to show waterwaves passing from deep into shallow water (they do not meet the boundary at 90°).

6. a) Copy and complete the diagrams opposite which show a ray of light travelling into a glass block.
   b) What happens to the speed of light when it passes from ...
   (i) Air into glass (ii) Glass into air.

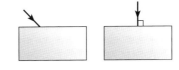

7. Copy and complete the following diagrams.

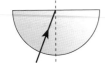
angle of incidence less than critical angle.

angle of incidence equal to critical angle.

angle of incidence greater than critical angle.

8. The diagram opposite shows an optical fibre. A ray of light enters one end of it.
   a) Copy and complete the path of the ray of light through the optical fibre.
   b) What is the name of the effect that occurs to the ray of light inside the fibre?
   c) Name and describe one use for optical fibres.

9. a) Copy and complete the following diagrams.

   b) What is the effect above called?

10. Draw diagrams to show ...
   a) the deviation of red light.
   b) the deviation of green light.
   c) the dispersion of white light by a glass prism.

11. a) The electromagnetic spectrum is made up of the following waves.

     INFRA-RED   GAMMA   MICROWAVES   LIGHT   X-RAYS   RADIOWAVES   ULTRAVIOLET

     Complete the table below, placing the waves in the correct order.

LONG WAVELENGTH							SHORT WAVELENGTH

    b) For EACH type of radiation name TWO USES.

12.

    A.   B.   C.   D.   E.

    Which of the above traces A to E shows ...
    (i) the quietest sound, (ii) the highest pitch, (iii) the loudest sound, (iv) the lowest pitch.

13. a) What are ultrasonic waves?
    b) Give two uses for ultrasonic waves.

14. a) (i) What are P Waves? (ii) What are S Waves?
    b) Draw a fully labelled diagram showing the path of P and S waves from an earthquake region.
    c) What can be deduced about the structure of the Earth from the study of P and S waves?

15. The diagram opposite shows the structure of the Earth.
    a) Name 'A', 'B', 'C' and 'D'.
    b) What evidence is there that 'A' has previously been subjected to very large forces?
    c) What evidence is there that the interior of the Earth is of a different material to 'A'?

16. Fill the spaces below using the following words: HEAT, TECTONIC PLATES, MANTLE, CRUST, RADIOACTIVE DECAY, CONVECTION CURRENTS.
    The Earth's _____ is 'cracked' into several large pieces called _____ which move slowly at speeds of a few cm per year driven by _____ in the _____ which are caused by _____ released from _____ .

17. What evidence is there for the 'Tectonic Plates' theory? Explain your answer by comparing the East Coast of South America and the West Coast of Africa.

18. The diagram below shows ocean floor spreading.
    a) What is A called?
    b) What is happening at B?
    c) What might be found in region C?
    d) What causes the movement shown by the arrows?

19. a) What are the consequences of two Tectonic Plates which slide past each other?
    b) Explain how it is possible for two Tectonic Plates to move away from each other.
    c) Explain what happens when two Tectonic Plates move towards each other.

Heat (thermal) energy is transferred from HOTTER PLACES TO COOLER PLACES by three different methods, CONDUCTION, CONVECTION and RADIATION.

Conduction

The key point about this type of energy transfer is that the SUBSTANCE ITSELF DOESN'T MOVE. Metals are particularly good conductors while INSULATORS (poor conductors) are also important.

Here is an example of an everyday appliance which uses both a conductor and an insulator.

REMEMBER! CONDUCTION HAPPENS MAINLY IN SOLIDS.

GOOD CONDUCTORS
● ALL METALS especially COPPER and ALUMINIUM
POOR INSULATORS

GOOD INSULATORS
● MOST NON-METALS
● GLASS ● WOOD
● PLASTIC
● ALL GASES
POOR CONDUCTORS

Convection

Liquids and gases can FLOW and can therefore transfer HEAT ENERGY from hotter to cooler areas by their own movement (see the diagrams below for the general idea).

Radiation

Energy is continually being transferred to and from all objects by radiation without particles of matter being involved. Hot objects transfer energy through INFRA-RED RADIATION and the hotter the object, the more energy it radiates.

● How much radiation is given out or taken in by an object depends on its SURFACE.

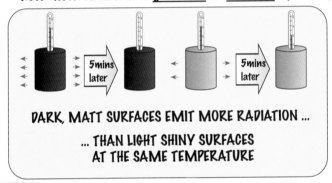
DARK, MATT SURFACES EMIT MORE RADIATION ...
... THAN LIGHT SHINY SURFACES AT THE SAME TEMPERATURE

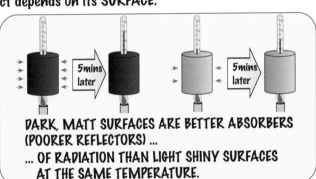
DARK, MATT SURFACES ARE BETTER ABSORBERS (POORER REFLECTORS) ...
... OF RADIATION THAN LIGHT SHINY SURFACES AT THE SAME TEMPERATURE.

――― HIGHER TIER ―――

Conduction – The Process

Conduction occurs in metals because as the metal becomes hotter its ions gain more kinetic energy. This energy is transferred to cooler parts of the metal by FREE ELECTRONS as they DIFFUSE through the metal, colliding with ions and other electrons.

POKER
CONDUCTION OF HEAT ENERGY

Convection – The Process

● As the liquid or gas gets hotter, its particles move faster causing it to EXPAND and become LESS DENSE than colder regions.
● The warm liquid or gas will now RISE UP and be replaced by COLDER, DENSER regions.

EXAMPLE A
Candle

EXAMPLE A shows red dye crystals placed in water over a heat source - a CONVECTION CURRENT is set up.
EXAMPLE B shows the circulation of air caused by a radiator - again, a CONVECTION CURRENT is set up.

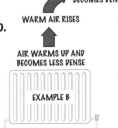
THE AIR COOLS AND BECOMES DENSER
WARM AIR RISES
THIS DENSER, COOLER AIR NOW SINKS
AIR WARMS UP AND BECOMES LESS DENSE
THIS COOLER AIR NOW REPLACES THE AIR WHICH IS RISING

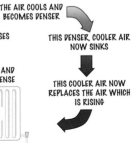
EXAMPLE B

Radiation – The Process

This transfer of energy takes place purely by WAVES - no particles of matter are involved eg. the Sun radiates heat energy to us across the vacuum of space.

Reducing Energy Consumption In Buildings

There are many different ways in which heat losses from a building can be reduced.

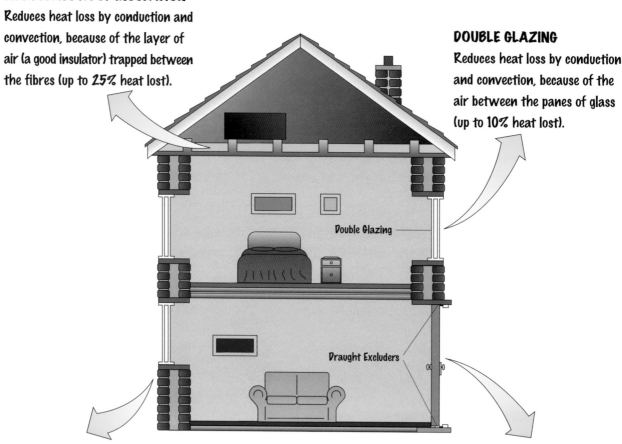

FIBREGLASS ROOF INSULATION
Reduces heat loss by conduction and convection, because of the layer of air (a good insulator) trapped between the fibres (up to 25% heat lost).

DOUBLE GLAZING
Reduces heat loss by conduction and convection, because of the air between the panes of glass (up to 10% heat lost).

Double Glazing

Draught Excluders

CAVITY WALL INSULATION
Reduces heat loss by conduction and especially convection by trapping the air in foam (up to 35% heat lost).

DRAUGHT EXCLUDERS
Reduces heat loss by convection by keeping as much warm air as possible inside (up to 15% heat lost).

Effectiveness And Cost-effectiveness Of Different Forms Of Insulation

Here is some typical data about the various methods of insulation above:

FORM OF INSULATION	ORIGINAL COST	ANNUAL AMOUNT SAVED	HOW LONG TO PAY FOR ITSELF
Roof Insulation	£400	£80	5 years
Cavity Wall Insulation	£600	£30	20 years
Double Glazing	£1,800	£60	30 years
Draught Excluders	£40	£20	2 years

The most EFFECTIVE of these methods is the one which saves the most money each year. In this case the ROOF INSULATION, with draught excluders being the least effective. However...

... to work out the most COST-EFFECTIVE we must consider the issue over a longer period of time, say 3 or 4 years. In this case, we can see that draught excluders have paid for themselves and are now well in profit. Nothing else has, so DRAUGHT EXCLUDERS are the most cost-effective.

Transfer Of Energy

When devices transfer energy, only part of it is USEFULLY TRANSFERRED to where it is wanted and in the form that it is wanted. The remainder is transferred in some non-useful way and is therefore 'wasted'. Here are four examples of the intended energy transfer and wastage in everyday devices.

1 TUNGSTEN FILAMENT LIGHT BULB.

ELECTRICAL
100 joules/sec

HEAT
80 joules/sec (wasted)

LIGHT
20 joules/sec (useful)

2 LOW ENERGY LIGHT BULB.

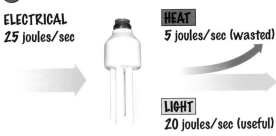

ELECTRICAL
25 joules/sec

HEAT
5 joules/sec (wasted)

LIGHT
20 joules/sec (useful)

3 ELECTRIC KETTLE.

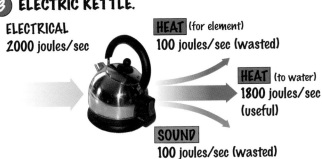

ELECTRICAL
2000 joules/sec

HEAT (for element)
100 joules/sec (wasted)

HEAT (to water)
1800 joules/sec
(useful)

SOUND
100 joules/sec (wasted)

4 ELECTRIC MOTOR (A DRILL INCLUDES ONE).

ELECTRICAL
500 joules/sec

HEAT
100 joules/sec (wasted)

KINETIC
300 joules/sec
(useful)

SOUND
100 joules/sec (wasted)

The 'wasted' energy and the 'useful' energy are both eventually transferred to the surroundings which become WARMER.
Unfortunately ...
... this energy becomes so spread out that it becomes difficult for any further useful energy transfers to occur.

Efficiency Of Devices

ELECTRICAL
200 joules/sec

HEAT
150 joules/sec

LIGHT
20 joules/sec

SOUND
30 joules/sec

The greater the proportion of energy supplied to a device, THAT IS USEFULLY TRANSFERRED, the more efficient we say the device is.

For example ...
... a car engine is 20% efficient - a lot more energy is wasted than is usefully transferred.
... a microwave is 60% efficient - more energy is usefully transferred than is wasted.

Calculating Efficiency

> Remember!
> A T.V. has both LIGHT and SOUND as useful energy transferred.

To calculate the efficiency of any device you need to use the following formula.

$$\text{EFFICIENCY} = \frac{\text{USEFUL ENERGY TRANSFERRED BY DEVICE}}{\text{TOTAL ENERGY SUPPLIED TO DEVICE}}$$

to convert it
to a percentage

In the case of the T.V. set shown, ... EFFICIENCY $= \dfrac{50}{200} \times \boxed{100} = 25\%$

Fuels

Fuels are substances which release useful amounts of energy when they burn.
Typical fuels used by humans for generating energy are ...

NON-RENEWABLE FOSSIL FUELS

... COAL   ... OIL   ... GAS   ... WOOD

Coal, oil and gas are energy resources which have formed over millions of years from the remains of living things.
For this reason they are called FOSSIL FUELS, and most of the energy used by humans comes from these sources.

- However, because these energy resources take so long to form, we are using them up at a far faster rate
  than they can be replaced. Hence they are called NON-RENEWABLE ENERGY RESOURCES,
  and will eventually run out.
- **NUCLEAR FUEL** is also a non-renewable, although unlike coal,
  oil and gas it is not a fossil fuel, and is not burnt to release energy.

AN IMPORTANT POINT!
- Wood is NOT a fossil fuel, nor is it non-renewable. It is classed as a renewable energy resource since,
  trees can be grown relatively quickly to replace those which are burnt to provide energy for heating.

Generating Electricity From Non-renewable Energy Resources

The trick in using non-renewables to generate electricity is to ...
... produce heat from the fuel, and use it to make steam which ...
... will eventually turn turbines attached to a generator.

Eg. ① Fossil fuels are burnt to release heat energy, ...
    ... which boils water to produce steam, ...
    ... which drives the turbines and ultimately the generators.

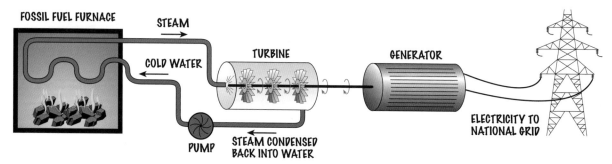

FOSSIL FUEL FURNACE   STEAM

COLD WATER   TURBINE   GENERATOR

PUMP   STEAM CONDENSED
BACK INTO WATER

ELECTRICITY TO
NATIONAL GRID

Eg. ② Electricity is also generated in a similar way ...
    ... using NUCLEAR FUEL
    eg. URANIUM and PLUTONIUM.
    Here a REACTOR is used to generate ...
    ... HEAT and a HEAT EXCHANGER is used ...
    ... to transfer this energy from the reactor ...
    ... to water which turns to steam ...
    to turn the turbines.

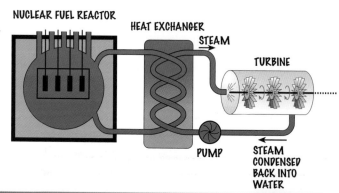

NUCLEAR FUEL REACTOR   HEAT EXCHANGER
STEAM
TURBINE

PUMP   STEAM
CONDENSED
BACK INTO
WATER

- RENEWABLE ENERGY RESOURCES are those that will not run out, because ...
  ... they are continually being replaced.
- This is because many of them are 'powered' by the Sun. For instance, the Sun causes evaporation which results in rain and flowing water, it causes convection currents which result in winds and these winds cause waves.
- Other types of energy resource rely on the gravitational pull of the moon! eg. tides.

Generating Electricity From Renewable Energy Resources

- In renewables, the energy resource is used to drive turbines directly.
  In other words, nothing needs to be burnt to produce heat!

WIND

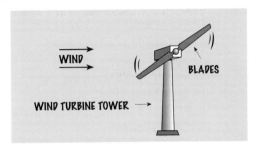

The force of the wind turns the blades of a wind turbine which in turn causes a generator to spin and produce electricity.

TIDAL

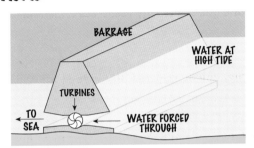

At high tide, water is trapped by a barrage. At low tide the water is released and flows back to the same level as the sea. The movement of this water drives a turbine to generate electricity.

WAVES

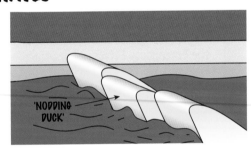

The rocking motion of the waves makes the 'nodding duck' move up and down. This movement is translated into a rotary movement which eventually turns a generator.

HYDRO-ELECTRIC

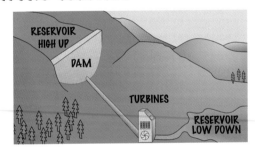

Water stored in reservoirs above the power station is allowed to flow down through pipes to drive the turbines. The water can be pumped back up again when the demand for electricity is low.

GEOTHERMAL

In some volcanic areas, hot water and steam rise naturally to the surface, having been heated up by the decay of radioactive substances (eg. uranium) within the earth. This steam can be used to drive turbines.

SOLAR

Solar cells rely on modern technology to transfer sunlight directly into useful electricity. This has applications in calculators, watches and garden lighting, as well as a more sophisticated use in space probes and satellites.

The four energy sources listed below are used to provide most of the electricity we need in this country directly through power stations. Some of the advantages and disadvantages of each one are listed below ...

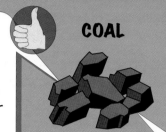

COAL

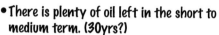

- Coal is relatively cheap and sometimes easy to obtain.
- Coal fired power stations are flexible in meeting demand and have a quicker start-up time than their nuclear equivalents.
- Estimates suggest that there may be over a century's worth of coal left.

- Burning produces carbon dioxide (CO_2) and sulphur dioxide (SO_2).
- CO_2 causes 'global warming' due to the Greenhouse Effect.
- Coal produces more CO_2 per unit of energy produced than oil or gas.
- SO_2 causes acid rain unless ...
  ... the sulphur is removed before burning ...
  ... or the SO_2 is removed from the waste gases. Both of these add to the cost.

OIL

- There is plenty of oil left in the short to medium term. (30yrs?)
- The price is often variable but it can be relatively easy to find.
- Oil fired Power Stations are flexible in meeting demand and have a quicker start-up time than both nuclear-powered and coal-fired reactors.

- Burning produces carbon dioxide and sulphur dioxide.
- CO_2 causes 'global warming' due to the Greenhouse Effect.
- Oil produces more CO_2 than gas, per unit of energy produced.
- SO_2 causes acid rain (see coal above).
- Oil is often carried between continents on tankers leading to the risk of spillage and pollution.

NATURAL GAS

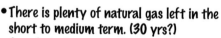

- There is plenty of natural gas left in the short to medium term. (30 yrs?)
- As relatively easy to find as oil.
- Gas fired power stations are flexible in meeting demand and have a quicker start-up time than nuclear, coal and oil.
- No sulphur dioxide (SO_2) is produced.

- Burning produces carbon dioxide (CO_2) although it is less than both coal and oil, per unit of energy produced.
- CO_2 causes 'global warming' due to the Greenhouse Effect.
- Expensive pipelines and networks are often required to transport it to the point of use.

NUCLEAR

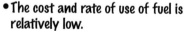

- The cost and rate of use of fuel is relatively low.
- They can often be situated in sparsely populated areas (and should be!)
- Nuclear power stations are flexible in meeting demand.
- They <u>don't</u> produce carbon dioxide and sulphur dioxide.

- Although there is very little escape of radioactive material in normal use, radioactive waste can stay dangerously radioactive for thousands of years and safe storage is expensive.
- HIGHER TIER — The cost of building and de-commissioning adds heavily to the unit cost of energy produced.
- They have the longest start-up time compared to coal, oil and gas.

Summary

ADVANTAGES

- Produce huge amounts of energy.
- They are reliable.
- They are flexible in meeting demand.
- They don't take up much space (relatively).

DISADVANTAGES

- They pollute the environment.
- They cause 'global warming' and acid rain.
- They will 'soon' run out.
- Fuels may have to be transported long distances.

The five energy sources listed below represent the attempts of modern technology to provide us with a clean, safe alternative source of energy. Some of the advantages and disadvantages of each one are listed below ...

WIND

- Wind turbines don't require any fuel and need very little maintenance.
- They don't produce any pollutant gases such as carbon dioxide and sulphur dioxide.
- Once they're built they give 'free' energy when the wind is blowing.

- You need loads of them usually on hills and coastal areas and this can look a bit ugly (visual pollution). Also, noise can be a problem.
- Electricity output depends entirely on the strength of the wind.
- Not very flexible in meeting demand unless the energy is stored.

TIDAL and WAVES

- These devices don't require any fuel.
- They don't produce any pollutant gases such as carbon dioxide and sulphur dioxide.
- Once they're built they provide 'free' energy - at certain times!
- Barrage water can be released when demand for electricity is high.

- Tidal barrages, across estuaries, are unsightly, a hazard to shipping, and destroy the habitats of wading birds etc.
- Output depends on daily variations in the state of the tide and monthly and annual variations in its height, in the case of tidal barrages, and the energy contained in the waves for the 'nodding duck'.

HYDRO-ELECTRIC

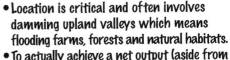

- No fuel is required unless they are operated in reverse to store energy.
- Very fast start-up time to meet sudden increases in demand.
- Large amounts of clean, reliable electricity can be produced.
- When operated in reverse, by pumping water into the higher reservoir, surplus electricity can be stored to help meet future peak demand.

- Location is critical and often involves damming upland valleys which means flooding farms, forests and natural habitats.
- To actually achieve a net output (aside from pumping) there must be adequate rainfall in the region where the reservoir is.

SOLAR

- Ideal for use in situations where a source of electricity is needed in a remote location.
- Excellent energy source when only a small amount of electricity is needed, eg. calculator, watch.
- When in direct sunlight they produce a 'free', clean, although small supply of electricity.

- The amount of electricity produced by solar cells depends on the intensity of light that falls on them. This means they're more useful in sunny places.
- Solar cells have a high cost per unit of electricity produced compared to all other sources except non-rechargeable batteries.

Summary

ADVANTAGES
- No chemical pollution.
- Often low maintenance.
- Don't contribute to 'global warming' and acid rain.
  ------- HIGHER TIER -------
- No fuel costs during operation.

DISADVANTAGES
- Take up lots of space and are unsightly.
- Unreliable (apart form H-E), weather dependent, and can't match demand.
- With the exception of hydro-electric they produce small amounts of electricity.
  ------- HIGHER TIER -------
- High initial capital outlay in building them.

Work

- When a FORCE MOVES an OBJECT ...
- ... WORK is DONE ON THE OBJECT resulting in the TRANSFER OF ENERGY where ...

WORK DONE (J) = ENERGY TRANSFERRED (J)

Work done, force and distance moved are related by the formula:

WORK DONE (J) = FORCE APPLIED (N) x DISTANCE MOVED IN DIRECTION OF FORCE (m)

EXAMPLE

A man pushes a car with a steady force of 250N.
The car moves a distance of 20m. How much work does he do?

250N PUSH

Using the formula: WORK DONE = FORCE APPLIED x DISTANCE MOVED IN DIRECTION OF FORCE

W = 250N x 20m

W = 5,000J (or 5KJ)

NB

When work is done on an elastic object to change its shape ...
... the energy is stored in the object as ELASTIC POTENTIAL ENERGY.

Power

- POWER is the RATE of TRANSFER OF ENERGY or the RATE at which WORK IS DONE.
- The GREATER the POWER, the MORE ENERGY that is transferred EVERY SECOND.

If two boys, Tom and Jim ...
... of the SAME WEIGHT ...
... race up the SAME HILL ...
... they both do the SAME AMOUNT ...
... of WORK to reach the top.

However ...
... since Tom has done the same amount of work as Jim but in a shorter time, then Tom has a GREATER POWER.

Power, work done and time taken are related by the formula:

$$\text{POWER (W or J/s)} = \frac{\text{WORK DONE (J)}}{\text{TIME TAKEN (s)}}$$

EXAMPLE

A crane lifts a load of 20,000N through a distance of 10m in 4s. Calculate the output power of the crane.
FIRSTLY WE NEED TO WORK OUT HOW MUCH WORK THE CRANE DOES AGAINST GRAVITY.

Using the formula: WORK DONE = FORCE APP. x DIST. MOVED

W = 20,000N x 10m

W = 200,000J

THE LOAD HAS NOW GAINED THIS AMOUNT OF ENERGY

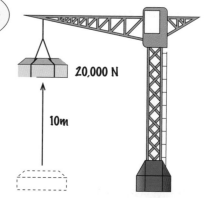

20,000 N

10m

Using the formula: $\text{POWER} = \dfrac{\text{WORK DONE}}{\text{TIME TAKEN}}$

$P = \dfrac{200,000J}{4s}$

= 50,000 W (or J/s)

or P = 50 KW ... SINCE 1KW = 1,000W

Weight

WEIGHT is due to the force of GRAVITY on an object.
* Near the surface of the Earth the
  GRAVITATIONAL FIELD STRENGTH (g) is 10N/Kg. ...
* ... so EVERY 1KG OF MATTER experiences a DOWNWARDS FORCE ...
  ... or has a WEIGHT of 10N.

EARTH'S SURFACE

↓ W = 10N   ↓ W = 20N   ↓ W = 50N

The formula:

WEIGHT (N) = MASS (kg) x GRAVITATIONAL FIELD STRENGTH (N/kg)

$$\frac{w}{m \times g}$$

—————————————— HIGHER TIER ——————————————

Gravitational Potential Energy

This is the ENERGY STORED in an object because of the HEIGHT ...
... through which the WEIGHT of the object has been LIFTED ...
... AGAINST the force of GRAVITY.
If an OBJECT CAN FALL ...
... IT'S GOT GRAVITATIONAL POTENTIAL ENERGY.

Calculating Change In Gravitational Potential Energy

The formula ...

CHANGE IN GRAVITATIONAL
POTENTIAL ENERGY (J) = WEIGHT (N) x CHANGE IN VERTICAL HEIGHT (m)

$$\frac{gpe}{mg \times \Delta h}$$

As you can see the formula triangle looks rather nasty, so we'll explain what it means ...
* CHANGE IN GRAVITATIONAL POTENTIAL ENERGY is represented as 'gpe.'
* WEIGHT is represented as 'mg' which is simply the mass, m, of an object multiplied by 'g' the gravitational field strength (see the top of the page).
* CHANGE IN VERTICAL HEIGHT is represented as Δh where Δ means 'change in'.

Anyway if you remember them as change in gravitational potential energy, weight and change in vertical height you can't go wrong.

EXAMPLE 1

A skier who weighs 800N takes the ski lift which takes him from a height of 1,000m to a height of 3,000m above ground. By how much does his gravitational potential energy change?
Using our formula:

CHANGE IN GRAV. POT. ENERGY = WEIGHT x CHANGE IN VERTICAL HEIGHT
= 800N x (3,000m - 1,000m)
= 800N x 2,000m
= 1,600,000J

This is an example of electrical energy being transferred as gravitational potential energy.

... and, as the skier has gone UP, it is an INCREASE IN GRAVITATIONAL POTENTIAL ENERGY.

EXAMPLE 2

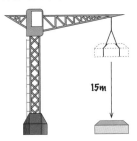

15m

A crane lowers a load of 25,000N from a height of 15m down to the ground. By how much does the gravitational potential energy of the load change?

Using our formula:

CHANGE IN GRAV. POT. ENERGY = WEIGHT x CHANGE IN VERTICAL HEIGHT
= 25,000N x (15m - 0m)
= 25,000N x 15m
= 375,000J

... and, as the load has gone DOWN, it is a DECREASE IN GRAVITATIONAL POTENTIAL ENERGY.

What Is Kinetic Energy?

- This is the ENERGY an object has because of its MOVEMENT.
- If it's MOVING, it's GOT KINETIC ENERGY.

It depends on two things ...   • THE MASS OF THE OBJECT (kg) and THE SPEED OF THE OBJECT (m/s)

- A moving car has kinetic energy as it has both MASS and SPEED.

- If the car now moves ...
  ... with a GREATER SPEED ...
  ... it has MORE KINETIC ENERGY ...
  ... <u>providing</u> its mass has not changed.

- However if we have a moving truck ...
  ... with a GREATER MASS ...
  ... it may have MORE KINETIC ENERGY ...
  ... even if its speed is less than that of the car!

Kinetic Energy – The Formula

The formula:

KINETIC ENERGY (J) $= \frac{1}{2} \times$ MASS (kg) $\times$ (SPEED)^2 (m/s)^2

EXAMPLE 1

A car of mass of 1,000kg is moving at a speed of 10m/s. How much kinetic energy does it have?

Using the formula: KINETIC ENERGY $= \frac{1}{2} \times$ MASS $\times$ (SPEED)^2

$= \frac{1}{2} \times$ 1,000kg $\times$ (10m/s)^2

$=$ 50,000J (or 50kJ)

EXAMPLE 2

If the truck above has a mass of 4,000 kg. Calculate it's speed if it has the SAME kinetic energy as the car in example 1.

Using the formula:
(which is rearranged
using the formula triangle)

$$(Speed)^2 = \frac{Kinetic\ energy}{\frac{1}{2} \times Mass}$$

$$(Speed)^2 = \frac{50,000J}{\frac{1}{2} \times 4,000kg} = 25$$

Speed $= \sqrt{25}$ (Need to SQUARE ROOT to get speed.)
Speed $=$ <u>5m/s.</u>

NB Since the truck has a GREATER MASS than the car then ...
... it can move at a SLOWER SPEED and have the SAME KINETIC ENERGY!

Magnets

All MAGNETS have a region of space around them called the MAGNETIC FIELD...
... which exerts a force on any magnetic material (eg. iron, steel) or on any other magnet, which enters it.
This force can be ...

iron or
steel bar

... ATTRACTIVE

... REPULSIVE

Electromagnets

If an ELECTRIC CURRENT flows through a COIL OF WIRE a MAGNETIC FIELD is formed around the coil...
... creating an ELECTROMAGNET. This is a MAGNET which can be SWITCHED ON and OFF.

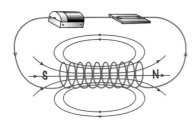

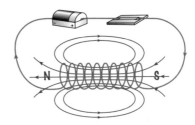

When the switch is closed...
... a current flows and a magnetic field is formed...
... which is very similar to that of a bar magnet.
One end becomes a north-seeking (N) pole...
... and the other end a south-seeking (S) pole.

However...
... if we reverse the direction of the current...
... this reverses the poles ...
... of the electromagnet formed.

NB

When the switch is open...
... a current no longer flows...
... and the magnetic field disappears.
The electromagnet is switched OFF.

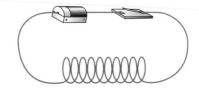

The Circuit Breaker

This is a safety device which uses an electromagnet.

'Soft' Iron

Contact

Coil

Current out

Current in   Pivot

Hinge

When the current through the COIL gets TOO HIGH...
... the strength of the magnetic field...
... generated by the electromagnet INCREASES until...
... it is strong enough to ATTRACT the SOFT IRON rocker.

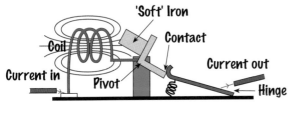

Contact broken

This causes the CONTACT TO BREAK...
... SWITCHING OFF THE CURRENT.

* See P.12 for an alternative diagram of a circuit breaker.

The Principle Of The Motor Effect

- When a wire carrying an **ELECTRIC CURRENT** is placed in a **PERMANENT MAGNETIC FIELD**...
- ... the magnetic field formed around the wire ...
- ... interacts with the permanent magnetic field...
- ... causing the wire to experience a force which causes it to move.

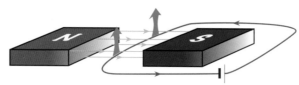

- The **SIZE** of the force on the wire can be increased by...

... INCREASING THE SIZE ...
... OF THE CURRENT ...
... (have more cells).

... INCREASING THE STRENGTH ...
... OF THE MAGNETIC FIELD ...
... (have stronger magnets).

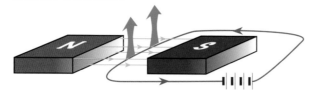
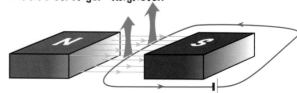

- The **DIRECTION** of the force on the wire can be reversed by...

... REVERSING THE DIRECTION ...
... OF FLOW OF THE CURRENT ...
... (turn your cell around).

... or REVERSING THE DIRECTION ...
... OF THE MAGNETIC FIELD ...
... (swap your magnets around).

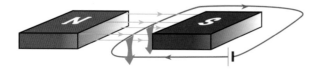
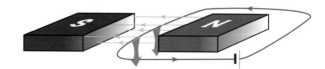

The Direct Current (d.c.) Motor

Electric motors form the basis of a vast range of electrical devices both in and out of the home.
These rely on the principle of the motor effect.

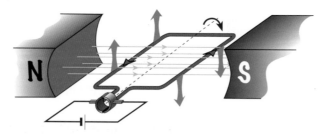

As a current flows through the coil a **MAGNETIC FIELD** is formed around the coil...
... creating an **ELECTROMAGNET**.
This magnetic field **INTERACTS** with the **PERMANENT MAGNETIC FIELD**...
... which exists between the **TWO POLES**, N and S.
A **FORCE** acts on both sides of the coil, which **ROTATES THE COIL** ...
... to give us a very simple motor.

GENERATORS

Making Electricity By Electromagnetic Induction

- If a wire or a coil of wire cuts through the lines of force of a magnetic field, or vice versa, ...
... then a VOLTAGE IS INDUCED (produced) between the ends of the wire ...
... and a CURRENT will be INDUCED in the wire if it is PART OF A COMPLETE CIRCUIT.

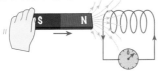

Moving the magnet INTO the coil ...
... induces a current in one direction.

A current can be induced in the opposite direction ...

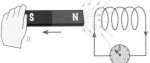

... by moving the magnet out of the coil OR ...

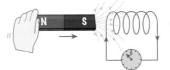

... by moving the other pole of the magnet into the coil.

- Generators use this principle for generating electricity by ...
... ROTATING A COIL OF WIRE WITHIN A MAGNETIC FIELD OR ROTATING A MAGNET INSIDE A COIL.
Both of these involve a magnetic field being cut by a coil of wire, creating an induced voltage.
However, if there is NO movement of magnet or coil there's no induced current.

In Electromagnetic induction, MOVEMENT PRODUCES CURRENT. This is really the opposite of what happens in the motor effect where CURRENT PRODUCES MOVEMENT.

Increasing The Size Of The Induced Voltage

The size of the induced voltage can be increased if we ...

1 Increase the **SPEED OF MOVEMENT** of the magnet or the coil.

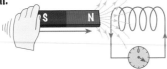

2 Increase the **STRENGTH OF THE MAGNETIC FIELD.**

3 Increase the **NUMBER OF TURNS** on the coil.

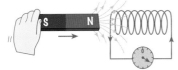

4 Increase the **AREA OF THE COIL.**

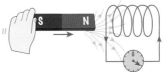

===== HIGHER TIER =====

The Alternating Current Generator

Very simply, A COIL OF WIRE IS ROTATED IN A MAGNETIC FIELD, and the same four principles for increasing the size of the induced voltage apply.
As the coil cuts through the magnetic field a current is INDUCED in the coil ...
... which is ALTERNATING ie. it reverses its direction of flow...
... every half turn of the coil, as can be seen below...

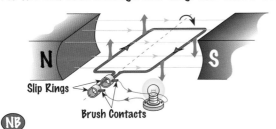

Slip Rings

Brush Contacts

CURRENT / TIME — and so on ...

NB THE BRUSH CONTACTS are spring-loaded so that they push gently against the SLIP RINGS in order that the circuit remains complete. Gradually they wear away and have to be replaced.

Distributing Electricity

Electricity generated at POWER STATIONS is distributed to homes, schools, shops, factories etc. all over the country by a network of cables called the NATIONAL GRID. Transformers are used to change the voltage of an a.c. supply, and are used both before and after transmission through the grid.

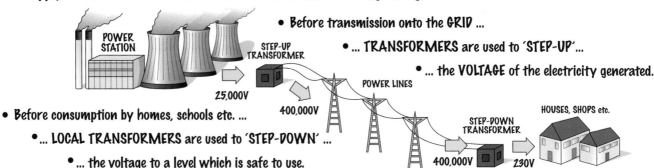

• Before transmission onto the GRID ...

     • ... TRANSFORMERS are used to 'STEP-UP'...

         • ... the VOLTAGE of the electricity generated.

POWER STATION

STEP-UP TRANSFORMER

POWER LINES

25,000V

400,000V

HOUSES, SHOPS etc.

STEP-DOWN TRANSFORMER

• Before consumption by homes, schools etc. ...

     • ... LOCAL TRANSFORMERS are used to 'STEP-DOWN' ...

         • ... the voltage to a level which is safe to use.

400,000V   230V

HIGHER TIER

Reducing The Energy Loss During Transmission

The HIGHER the CURRENT that passes through ANY WIRE the greater the AMOUNT OF ENERGY LOST AS HEAT FROM THE WIRE. So we need to transmit as low a current as possible through the POWER LINES.

But since, POWER = VOLTAGE × CURRENT (See P.9)

... the smaller the current, the higher the voltage, needed to transmit energy at the same rate!
This is where transformers come in.

Low voltage, high current for domestic consumption.

STEP-UP TRANSFORMER FOR TRANSMISSION

CURRENT

VOLTAGE

VOLTAGE

High voltage, low current, small energy loss as heat during transmission.

STEP-DOWN TRANSFORMER FOR CONSUMPTION

CURRENT

How Transformers Work

Transformers consist of ...
• Two COILS called the PRIMARY COIL and the SECONDARY COIL wrapped around a SOFT IRON CORE.

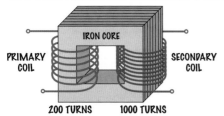

IRON CORE

PRIMARY COIL   SECONDARY COIL

200 TURNS   1000 TURNS

... an example of a STEP-UP TRANSFORMER.

Transformers work because ...
• An ALTERNATING INPUT VOLTAGE across the PRIMARY COIL ...
• ... causes an ALTERNATING CURRENT (a.c) ...
• ... to flow through the PRIMARY COIL.
• This alternating current creates a continually changing ...
• ... MAGNETIC FIELD which expands and collapses across ...
• ... the SECONDARY COIL INDUCING an ALTERNATING OUTPUT VOLTAGE.

THE SIZE OF THE OUTPUT (OR SECONDARY) VOLTAGE DEPENDS ON THE RELATIVE NUMBER OF TURNS ON THE PRIMARY AND SECONDARY COILS.

In general the formula is ...

$$\frac{\text{VOLTAGE ACROSS PRIMARY (V), } V_p}{\text{VOLTAGE ACROSS SECONDARY (V), } V_s} = \frac{\text{NUMBER OF TURNS ON PRIMARY, } N_p}{\text{NUMBER OF TURNS ON SECONDARY, } N_s}$$

EXAMPLE

A voltage of 230V is applied to the primary coil in the above diagram. What is the voltage across the secondary coil?

Using our formula: $\dfrac{V_p}{V_s} = \dfrac{N_p}{N_s}$

$$\frac{230V}{V_s} = \frac{200}{1000}$$

(if we rearrange) $V_s = \dfrac{230 \times 1000}{200} = 1150 \text{ volts}$

... OR, since there are five times more turns on the secondary coil, V_s will be FIVE TIMES V_p ...
... ie. $V_s = 5 \times V_p = 5 \times 230V = 1150V$

TYPES, EFFECTS AND USES OF RADIATION

THE THREE TYPES ...

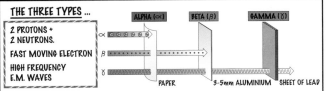

2 PROTONS + 2 NEUTRONS.

FAST MOVING ELECTRON

HIGH FREQUENCY E.M. WAVES

ALPHA (α) BETA (β) GAMMA (γ)

PAPER   3-5mm ALUMINIUM   SHEET OF LEAD

These are known as IONISING RADIATION because collisions between them and neutral ATOMS result in the formation of ions.

DANGERS ... Damage to cells through ionisation can cause CANCER. Only β and γ can penetrate the tissues from outside of the body, but from inside (eg. inhalation into the lungs) α is the most dangerous since it the most strongly ionising. Workers in the nuclear industry wear safety badges containing photographic film.

USES OF RADIOACTIVE ISOTOPES ...

Sterilisation of medical instruments using gamma rays.
Cancer treatment using gamma rays in careful doses.
Controlling thickness in paper mills.
Tracing leaks, and passage of substances in living things.

STRUCTURE OF THE ATOM & RADIOACTIVE DECAY

Rutherford and Marsden performed the 'scattering experiment' which showed the existence of a region of positive charge at the centre of the atom.

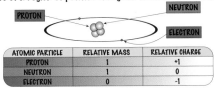

PROTON   NEUTRON   ELECTRON

ATOMIC PARTICLE	RELATIVE MASS	RELATIVE CHARGE
PROTON	1	+1
NEUTRON	1	0
ELECTRON	0	-1

MASS NUMBER (Nucleon number) = No of protons and neutrons.
PROTON NUMBER = No of protons (which is equal to the no. of electrons).
ISOTOPES ... are atoms with the same number of protons but a different number of neutrons, some of which are radioactive and called RADIOISOTOPES or RADIONUCLIDES.

RADIOACTIVE DECAY ...

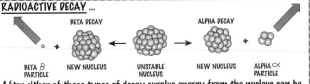

BETA DECAY   ALPHA DECAY

BETA β PARTICLE   NEW NUCLEUS   UNSTABLE NUCLEUS   NEW NUCLEUS   ALPHA α PARTICLE

After either of these types of decay surplus energy from the nucleus can be given off as GAMMA RADIATION.

DATING OF MATERIALS AND NUCLEAR FISSION

The older a material is, the less radiation it emits.
The HALF-LIFE of a material is the time it takes ...
• ... for half the atoms to decay.
• ... for the count rate to fall to half.

HALF-LIFE   HALF-LIFE   HALF-LIFE

This idea can be used to date certain materials using radioisotopes such as uranium 239 or Potassium 40. You must first work out how many half lives it would take to reduce the amount of radioisotope to its current level in the sample. If it takes three half lives then you would multiply the half-life of the radioisotope by 3.

NUCLEAR FISSION is used to produce energy in nuclear reactors. A neutron collides with a uranium nucleus causing it to split into 2 smaller nuclei with the release of further neutrons which can then cause further fission of uranium atoms.

Although there are dangers with this, an incredibly large amount of energy is produced.

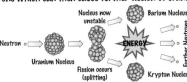

Nucleus now unstable   Barium Nucleus

Neutron   ENERGY   Further Neutrons

Uranium Nucleus   Fission occurs (splitting)   Krypton Nucleus

1. a) What are the three types of radiation?
   b) Which type of radiation ...
   (i) can pass through paper but not aluminium?
   (ii) was used by Rutherford in his scattering experiment?
   (iii) is part of the electromagnetic spectrum?
   (iv) cannot pass through paper?

2. The diagram opposite shows a paper mill where radiation is used to control the thickness of paper.
   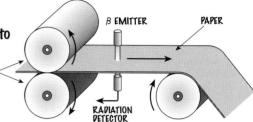
   a) Why must β radiation be used and not α or γ ?
   b) If the paper thickness becomes too thin what would happen to the reading on the radiation detector? Explain your answer.

3. a) What is ionisation?
   b) Why are α, β and γ called ionising radiation?
   c) What damage will α, β and γ radiation do to healthy cells?

4. a) What is the plum pudding model of the atom? Draw a fully labelled diagram.
   b) The diagram shows the basics of the scattering experiment performed by Rutherford.

   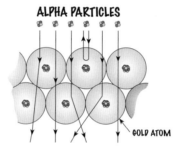

   (i) Why must the gold foil be only a few atoms thick?
   (ii) Why was the gold foil bombarded by alpha particles?
   (iii) Some α particles were deflected back towards the source. What did this prove?

5. a) What is an isotope?
   b) Three isotopes of oxygen are A) $^{16}_{8}O$ B) $^{17}_{8}O$ and C) $^{18}_{8}O$
   (i) Which isotope contains the greatest number of neutrons?
   (ii) What do all three isotopes have in common?

6. a) What is an alpha particle?
   b) What is a beta particle?
   c) What is a gamma ray?

7. a) A radioisotope has a half-life of 2 hours. What fraction of the parent atoms (ie. those that have not decayed) will remain after (i) 2 hours (ii) 8 hours (iii) one day?
   b) A sample of igneous rock is found to contain equal amounts of lead and uranium. If the half-life of uranium is 700,000,000 years calculate the age of the rock.
   c) If another sample of igneous rock is 2,800,000,000 years old, what proportion of uranium does it contain compared to lead?

8. a) What is nuclear fission?
   b) What is a chain reaction?
   c) Why is it such a controversial energy source?

THE COMPLETE KEY STAGE 3 PACKAGE ...

... 3 Course books

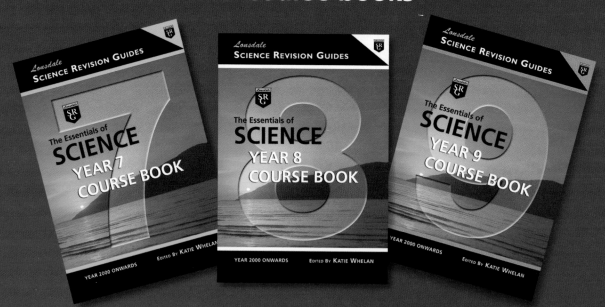

... matched perfectly to the QCA exemplar scheme of work for Key Stage 3.
All the content ... lots of exercises ... and an investigation for each unit.
These course books provide an inspection-proof scheme of work
for over-worked Science Departments.
Also there are 300 pages of differentiated internet support!

Plus ... the world famous **Revision Guide** and **Student Worksheets**.
These pull together all the information pupils need from years 7, 8 and 9 for
their Key Stage 3 National Curriculum Tests. They are completely revised and
updated for the new National Curriculum and contain everything the pupil
needs to revise ... and nothing more.